INTRODUCTION TO THE UNITED STATES AIR FORCE MUSEUM

The U.S. Air Force Museum is the oldest and largest military aviation museum in the world. It began in 1923 at McCook Field near downtown Dayton as a collection of U.S. and foreign WWI aircraft and related equipment items. In 1927 with the closing of McCook Field, the artifacts were moved to Wright Field and exhibited in a corner of a laboratory building. Five years later, the collection was renamed the Army Aeronautical Museum. Under the Works Progress Administration, a new Museum building was constructed in 1935 and opened at Wright Field. It was closed to the public in 1940 and converted to wartime office use a short time later.

In 1948, the Air Force Technical Museum opened in a former engine overhaul facility, but it was not until 1955 that the public was permitted access to the collection. In 1954, the Museum received permission to acquire and display full-size aircraft. In 1956, it officially became the Air Force Museum. Since the World War II engine overhaul building was neither permanent nor fireproof, the Museum required a new facility to meet its needs. Through the efforts of the Air Force Museum Foundation, Inc., and the generosity of many contributors, the Museum moved into its new home in 1971. A new Visitor Reception Center dedicated in 1976 added much needed space for the lobby area and permitted expansion of the restaurant, souvenir shop and bookstore facilities.

During the summer of 1977 the Museum Annex was opened on the historic old Wright Field Flight Line. Hangars 1 and 9 were made available to the Museum to house and protect about forty aircraft. These supplementary hangars, now called the Presidential Collection Hangar and the R&D Test & Evaluation Hangar, are located near the main museum.

A further addition, funded jointly by the federal government and the Museum Foundation, was opened in May 1988. The Modern Flight Hangar nearly doubled the size of the Museum at that time. Currently it is the home of the Museum's Korean War and Southeast Asia/Vietnam War aircraft and exhibits.

An IMAX Theatre and new atrium-style lobby were opened in May 1991. The dramatic new six-story screen theatre adds a unique new experience for the museum visitor.

In 2003, the Museum opened the Eugene Kettering Building which houses aircraft of the Cold War and post Cold War period.

The Museum presents the history of the United States Air Force and predecessor organizations by exhibiting aircraft, missiles, and artifacts associated with important events and eras, notable achievements and aeronautical developments.

TABLE OF CONTENTS

PROLOGUE

For thousands of years man dreamed of flying. In 1783 he finally realized his dream by flying for the first time in a hot air balloon in France. On December 17, 1903, two enterprising young brothers from Dayton, Ohio, flew the first successful controlled, powered flight in a heavier-than-air aircraft at Kittyhawk, North Carolina.

The Wright brothers felt their new "flying machine" would be of value to the U.S. Army. In 1909 the Army bought the world's first military aircraft from the brothers.

It has been a hundred years since the Wright brothers' first flight at Kittyhawk. Since that time America's inventory of military aircraft has grown tremendously in numbers and technology. The United States Air Force Museum is tasked with telling the story of this remarkable growth, not only by exhibiting hundreds of Air Force aircraft from throughout this period, but also by telling the story of the thousands of military personnel who supported these amazing flying machines.

Representing a century of aviation progress, a 1911 Wright Flyer is suspended above the YF-22 of the 21st Century (USAFM/Fisher)

WRIGHT 1909 MILITARY FLYER

This airplane is an exact reproduction of the Wright 1909 Military Flyer. Upon being purchased by the Signal Corps for $30,000 on August 2, 1909, the original airplane was redesignated Signal Corps Airplane No. 1, the world's first military heavier–than–air flying machine. It was used in October 1909 for giving flight instruction to Lts. Frank P. Lahm and Frederic E. Humphreys, and in 1910 it was used by Lt. Benjamin D. Foulois to teach himself how to fly. By March 1911, the airplane was no longer fit for use and was retired. It is now in the collection of the Smithsonian Institution, Washington, D.C.

This reproduction was constructed in 1955 by personnel of the U.S. Air Force Museum. It is equipped with an engine donated by Mr. Orville Wright and chains, sprockets, and propellers donated by the heirs of the Wright estate.

SPECIFICATIONS

Span: 36 ft. 6 in.
Length: 28 ft. 11 in.
Height: 7 ft. 10 1/2 in.
Weight: 740 lbs.
Engine: Four cylinder Wright of 30.6 hp.
Cost: $25,000 plus $5,000 bonus

PERFORMANCE

Maximum speed: 42 mph.
Maximum endurance: 1 hr. (approx)

CURTISS 1911 MODEL D

This airplane is a reproduction of the Curtiss 1911 Model D Type IV pusher, the second military airplane purchased by the U.S. Army Signal Corps. Known as Signal Corps Airplane No. 2, it was accepted at Fort Sam Houston, Texas, on April 27, 1911, one of five airplanes ordered by the Army that year. The military Model D is similar to the Curtiss Standard D pusher, having a tricycle landing gear and interplane ailerons, but the ailerons are attached to the rear instead of the front interplane struts. The wings were made in sections, making the airplane easy to disassemble and transport on Army wagons. The pilot operates the ailerons with a shoulder yoke on his seat, and the front elevator and rear rudder with the wheel mounted on a column in front of him. An observer's seat is located behind the pilot.

This reproduction was constructed in 1985–1987 by U.S. Air Force Museum personnel. They relied heavily on measurements scaled from early photographs of the original Signal Corps No. 2 because original drawings and adequate written descriptions were not available. Additional details were gathered from an existing factory–built Curtiss pusher and from recent drawings. Except for the engine, which is made of wood and plastic, all materials used in the reproduction are essentially the same as those used in the original.

CURTISS JN–4D "JENNY"

The Curtiss "Jenny," America's most famous World War I airplane, was developed by combining the best features of the Curtiss "J" and "N" models. A 1915 version, the JN–3, was used in 1916 during Pershing's Punitive Expedition into Mexico. Its poor performance, however, made it unsuited for field operations.

The JN–3 was modified in 1916 to improve its performance and redesignated the JN–4. With America's entry into World War I on April 6, 1917, the Signal Corps began ordering large quantities of JN–4s, and by the time production was terminated after the Armistice, more than 6,000 had been delivered, the majority of them the JN–4D.

The Jenny was generally used for primary flight training, but some were equipped with machine guns and bomb racks for advanced training. After World War I, hundreds were sold on the civilian market. The airplane soon became the mainstay of the "Barnstormer" of the 1920s, and some Jennies were still being flown in the 1930s.

The JN–4D now on display was obtained from Mr. Robert Pfiel of Taylor, Texas, in 1956.

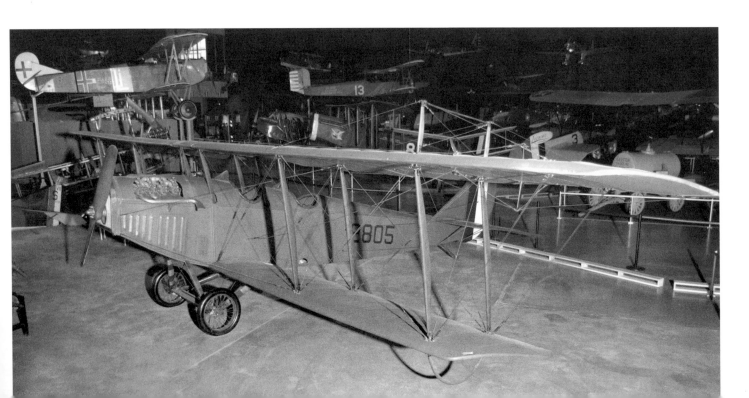

SPECIFICATIONS

Span: **43 ft. 7 in.**
Length: 27 ft. 4 in.
Height: 9 ft. 10 in.
Weight: 1,430 lbs.
Armament: Usually none
Engine: Curtiss OX-5 of 90 hp.
Cost: $5,465

PERFORMANCE

Maximum speed: 75 mph.
Maximum endurance: 2 1/2 hrs.

SPECIFICATIONS

Span: 26 ft. 3 in.
Length: 20 ft. 4 in.
Height: 8 ft.
Weight: 1,625 lbs. loaded
Armament: Two Vickers .303 cal. machine guns
Engine: Gnome 9–N rotary of 160 hp.
Crew: One

PERFORMANCE

Maximum speed: 122 mph
Service ceiling: 17,000 ft.
Range: 180 miles

NIEUPORT N.28C–1 "NIEUPORT 28"

The Nieuport 28 (N.28C-1) was the first fighter airplane flown in combat by pilots of the American Expeditionary Forces (AEF) in WW I. Its second armed patrol with an AEF unit on April 14, 1918, resulted in two victories when Lts. Alan Winslow and Douglas Campbell (who later became the first American–trained ace) of the 94th Aero Squadron each downed an enemy aircraft. Although the Nieuport 28 was considered obsolete at the time, American pilots maintained a favorable ratio of victories to losses with it. The Nieuport was more maneuverable than the sturdier SPAD XIII that replaced it, but the Nieuport had a tendency to shed its upper wing fabric during high speed dives. Even so, many American aces of WW I flew the French–built Nieuport at one time or another in their careers.

This reproduction was rebuilt by Museum personnel. It contains wood and hardware from an original Nieuport 28. The aircraft is painted and marked to represent a Nieuport of the 95th Aero Squadron, 3rd Flight, as it appeared in July 1918. It was placed on display in May 1994.

HALBERSTADT CL IV

The Halberstadt CL IV was developed to replace the earlier CL II model as a principle ground attack aircraft for the German army. First introduced to combat in early 1918 in time for the last great German offensive of the First World War, the CL IV proved to be very successful in attacking Allied positions ahead of the advancing German troops. Equipped with both fixed and flexible machine guns as well as hand dropped grenades and small bombs, the CL IV was very effective in this role, but it lacked armor which became necessary as Allied ground fire became increasingly effective against low-flying aircraft. The CL IV was one of the most sought after targets of Allied pursuit squadrons, but it was able to give a very good account of itself in a dogfight. A versatile machine, the CL IV also did yeoman duty as an intercepter against Allied night bombing raids and served as a night bomber against troop concentrations and airfields near the front lines.

The Halberstadt CL IV on display was acquired by the USAF Museum in 1984. It was badly deteriorated at the time, and its subsequent restoration was completed as a joint international cooperative venture by the Museum für Verkehr und Technik in Berlin, Germany, the National Air and Space Museum of the Smithsonian Institution, and the United States Air Force Museum. It is marked as the CL IV of the squadron leader of Schlachtstaffel 21 which is known to have engaged elements of the U.S. Army's 94th and 95th Aero Squadrons in mid-July 1918 during the Chateau Thierry campaign.

SPECIFICATIONS

Span: 35 ft. 2 7/8 in.
Length: 21 ft. 5 1/2 in.
Height: 8 ft. 9 1/8 in.
Weight: 2,350 lbs. loaded
Armament: One or two 9mm fixed Spandau Machine guns and one Parabellum 9mm flexible machine gun; anti-personnel grenades and four or five 22 lb. bombs.
Engine: One Mercedes D III six cylinder in-line, water-cooled engine of 160 hp.
Crew: Two

PERFORMANCE

Maximum speed: 103 mph.
Endurance: 3.5 hours

SPECIFICATIONS

Span: 26 ft. 6 in.
Length: 20 ft. 6 in.
Height: 8 ft. 6 in.
Weight: 1,888 lbs.
Armament: Two Vickers .303 cal. machine guns. It could also carry four 25 lb. bombs.
Engine: 200 hp. or 220 hp. Hispano-Suiza water cooled engine.

PERFORMANCE

Maximum speed: 135 mph.
Ceiling: 20,000 ft.
Range: 250 statute miles/ 217 nautical miles.

SPAD XIII

The SPAD XIII was designed in 1916 as a French attempt to counter the twin gun German fighters like the Halberstadt. The SPAD XIII doubled the firepower of the earlier SPAD VII by using two Vickers .303 cal. machine guns with 400 rounds of ammunition for each gun. The enthusiasm of the French pilots who tested the aircraft between April and September 1917 encouraged the French government to order more than 2,000. The U.S. Air Service also began flying the SPAD XIII in March 1918, and by war's end in November 1918, the Air Service had acquired 893. Throughout 1917 and into 1918 the SPAD XIII held its own against German aircraft, but in the summer of 1918 it was outclassed by the newly arrived Fokker D.VII. The SPAD XIII had poor visibility and insufficient rate of climb, but it proved itself a rugged fighter with the ability to dive at high speed to escape enemy planes.

This airplane was built in November 1918 and after the war was shipped to the U.S. The late Cole Palen acquired the aircraft in 1951 and first flew it in 1956. It was rebuilt in 1988 for static display and given the 95th Pursuit Squadron markings. The Museum obtained the aircraft through a bequest upon Cole Palen's death in 1993. It arrived in April 1996 and will be restored to represent the SPAD XIII flown by Captain Eddie Rickenbacker, America's WWI "Ace of Aces".

FOKKER Dr. I

Few aircraft of the World War I period have received the attention given the Fokker Dr. I triplane. Often linked with the career of the highest scoring ace of that war, Germany's Rittmeister Manfred von Richthofen, the nimble Dr. I earned a reputation as one of the best "dogfighters" of the war.

The Fokker Dr. I was ordered into production on July 14, 1917, in response to the success earlier that year of the British Sopwith Triplane. The first Dr.Is appeared over the Western Front in August 1917. Pilots were impressed with its maneuverability, and several, including von Richthofen, soon scored victories with the highly maneuverable triplane. Nineteen of Richthofen's last 21 victories were achieved while he was flying a Dr. I.

Fokker built 320 Dr.1s. For a brief period production was suspended while the wings were redesigned to prevent in-flight failures. By May 1918, the Dr. I was being replaced by the newer and faster Fokker D VII.

No original Fokker Dr.Is have survived. This reproduction is painted to represent the aircraft flown by Lt. Arthur Rahn in April 1918, when he served with Jagdstaffel 19. Rahn is credited with six confirmed victories The aircraft was placed on display in April 1994.

SPECIFICATIONS

Span: 23 ft. 7 in.
Length: 18 ft. 11 in.
Height: 9 ft. 8 in.
Weight: 891 lbs. empty/
1,291 lbs. loaded
Armament: Two 7.92mm Spandau LMG 08/15 machine guns.
Engine: Oberursel Ur II of 110 hp. or LeRhone 110 hp.
Crew: One

PERFORMANCE

Maximum speed: 115 mph./
100 knots
Range: 185 statute miles/
161 nautical miles
Service ceiling: 23,000 ft.

SPECIFICATIONS

Span: 26 ft. 9 in.
Length: 20 ft. 11 in.
Height: 9 ft. 6 in.
Weight: 2,100 lbs.
Armament: None
Engine: Wright–Hispano E of 180 hp.
Crew: One

PERFORMANCE

Maximum speed: 122 mph.
Cruising speed: 90 mph.
Range: 225 miles
Service ceiling: 17,000 ft.

EBERHART SE–5E

The SE–5E is an American–built version of the WW I S.E.5a designed by the Royal Aircraft Factory in Britain. The prototype S.E.5 first flew in December 1916, and deliveries of production S.E.5s began in March 1917. S.E.5a deliveries followed in June 1917. The S.E.5, noted for its strength, stability and speed, is said to have rivaled the Sopwith Camel as the most successful British fighter of WW I. The American Expeditionary Force bought 38 S.E.5a's in Britain and the design was selected for U.S. production. Orders were placed with the Curtiss Aeroplane and Motors Corp. but the Armistice halted production and only one Curtiss S.E.5a was completed. Fifty–six more were assembled from components shipped from Britain. In the 1922–1923 period, 50 versions of the S.E.5a, now known as the SE–5E, were assembled in the U.S. by the Eberhart Steel Products Co. from spare parts it had produced. The Air Service used SE–5Es primarily for training.

The Museum acquired this SE–5E through a donation by the estate of Lt. Col. William C. Lambert, USAF (Ret.), a WW I ace (21 1/2 victories) who flew the S.E.5a as an American member of the Royal Flying Corps and the Royal Air Force. The Air Force Museum Foundation also helped buy the aircraft. The Museum restored it as an SE–5E of the 18th Hq. Sqdn., Bolling Field, D.C. circa 1925.

PACKARD LePERE LUSAC 11

Designed during 1917 by Captain Georges LePere, a French aeronautical engineer working for the U.S. Army Air Service, the LUSAC 11 was the result of efforts to get an American built fighter into combat as soon as possible. The acronym "LUSAC" stood for LePere United States Army Combat. Designed to be a combination fighter and reconnaissance aircraft, it carried a pilot and an observer/gunner. The aircraft was designed by LePere to perform as well if not better than similar combat aircraft then in use.

Captain LePere, along with several other French aviation engineers, began work on the new design in January 1918. The Packard Motor Car Company of Detroit, Michigan, provided design and fabrication space and additional engineers. The first of three prototypes was completed on April 30, 1918. It was then flown to Wilbur Wright Field, Ohio for flight tests. These tests began on May 15 and were flown by several test pilots who were generally satisfied with the LUSAC 11's performance. Although the Bureau of Aircraft Production ordered 28 more aircraft, the LUSAC 11s were too late to see service in WWI, but were used at McCook Field in the 1920s for high-altitude research.

SPECIFICATIONS

Span: 41 ft. 7 in.
Length: 25 ft. 3 in.
Height: 10 ft. 7 in.
Weight: 3,746 lbs. loaded
Armament: Two .30 cal. Marlin and two .30 cal Lewis machine guns.

Engine: Liberty 12 of 400 hp.
Crew: Two

PERFORMANCE

Maximum speed: 136 mph./ 123 knots.
Cruising Speed: 118 mph./ 107 knots
Range: 320 statute miles/ 289 nautical miles
Service ceiling: 20,200 ft.

SPECIFICATIONS

Span: 29 ft. 3 1/2 in.
Length: 22 ft. 11 1/2 in.
Height: 9 ft. 2 1/2 in.
Weight: 1,540 lbs. empty,
1,939 lbs. loaded
Armament: Two 7.92mm Spandau machine guns
Engine: Mercedes 160 hp or BMW 185 hp
Crew: One

PERFORMANCE

Maximum speed: Mercedes engine: 120mph, BMW engine: 124 mph.
Service ceiling: Mercedes engine: 18,000 ft., BMW engine: 21,000 ft.

FOKKER D.VII

First appearing over the World War I battlefield in May 1918, the Fokker D. VII quickly showed its superior performance over Allied fighters. With its high rate of climb, higher ceiling, and excellent handling characteristics, the German pilots were able to score 565 victories over Allied aircraft during August 1918.

Designed by Reinhold Platz, the D.VII was chosen over several other designs during a competition held in January and February 1918. Baron Manfred von Richthofen, the famous Red Baron, flew the prototype designated V.11. He found it easy to fly, able to dive at high speed, yet remain steady as a rock, and possessing good visibility. His recommendation virtually decided the competition. To achieve higher production rates, both the Albatros company and the Allgemeine Elektrizitats Gesellschaft (A.E.G.), also built the D.VII. By war's end in November 1918, these three companies had built more than 1,700 aircraft.

The aircraft on display, a reproduction, is painted to represent the Fokker D.VII of Lt Rudolf Stark, squadron leader of Jasta 35b in October 1918. It was placed on exhibit in May 1996.

CONSOLIDATED PT–1 "TRUSTY"

The PT–l, procured by the Army Air Service in 1925, established the basic design for primary trainers into the World War II period. It was also the first airplane purchased in substantial quantity following World War I, with 221 being delivered from production. It was used extensively during the late 1920s and early 1930s for training aviation cadets in California and Texas.

Developed from the Dayton–Wright TW–3 airplane, the PT–1 featured an innovation for trainers, a welded fuselage framework of chrome–molybdenum steel tubing providing greater structural strength. The airplane was so sturdy and dependable that it was nicknamed the "Trusty." However, it was so easy to fly that it bred overconfidence in some of the student pilots, an undesirable trait for men who were soon to be flying faster airplanes having more difficult handling characteristics.

The airplane on display was obtained from the Ohio State University in 1957.

SPECIFICATIONS

Span: 34 ft. 9 1/2 in.
Length: 27 ft. 8 in.
Height: 9 ft. 6 in.
Weight: 2,550 lbs. loaded
Armament: None
Engine: Wright "E" of 180 hp. (Hispano–Suiza design)
Cost: $8,000

PERFORMANCE

Maximum speed: 99 mph.
Cruising speed: 78 mph.
Range: 310 miles
Service ceiling: 13,450 ft.

SPECIFICATIONS

Span: 45 ft. 0 in.
Length: 34 ft. 7 in.
Height: 12 ft. 1 in.
Weight: 5,000 lbs. maximum
Armament: (for standard OA–1A)
One forward–firing and two
flexible .30–caliber machine guns.
Engine: Liberty V–1650
of 425 hp.
Cost: $21,000

PERFORMANCE

Maximum speed: 122 mph.
Cruising speed: 90 mph.
Range: 750 miles
Service ceiling: 13,500 ft.

LOENING OA–1A

In 1923, Grover Loening designed a unique observation amphibian aircraft powered by an inverted Liberty engine. First designated the COA–1, it combined features of both a landplane and seaplane by merging the fuselage and hull into a single structure, eliminating the hanging floats and the elevated engine of a seaplane. Between 1924 and 1928, the Army ordered 45 OA–1s primarily for use in the Hawaiian and Philippine Islands and regions with numerous lakes and large rivers. Of these, 15 were OA–1As.

The "San Francisco" on display was one of five OA–1As which on Dec. 21, 1926, embarked from San Antonio, Texas, on a 22,000–mile Pan American Good Will tour of 25 Central and South American countries which lasted until May 2, 1927. Its pilots were Capt. Ira C. Eaker and Lt. Muir S. Fairchild. The MacKay Trophy and Distinguished Flying Cross were awarded to all the fliers who made this flight.

This OA–1A is on loan from the National Air and Space Museum of the Smithsonian Institution.

CURTISS P–6E "HAWK"

The P–6E, a first–line pursuit aircraft of the early 1930s, was the last of the fighter biplanes built in quantity for the Army Air Corps. Originally designated the Y1P–22, it was later redesignated the P–6E because of its similarity to other P–6 series airplanes. Although it was never used in combat, it is remembered as one of the most beautiful biplanes ever built. Despite its excellent performance, only 46 P–6Es were ordered because of the shortage of funds for the Air Corps during the austere days of the Depression.

This P–6E appears in the colors and markings of the airplane assigned in 1933 to Captain Ross G. Hoyt, Commanding Officer of the 17th Pursuit Squadron, 1st Pursuit Group, based at Selfridge Field, Michigan. It was donated by Mr. Edward S. Perkins of Anniston, Alabama, and restored by the Department of Aviation Technology, Purdue University in 1963.

SPECIFICATIONS

Span: 31 ft. 6 in.
Length: 23 ft. 2 in.
Height: 8 ft. 11 in.
Weight: 3,432 lbs. loaded
Armament: Two .30–cal. machine guns
Engine: Curtiss V–1570 of 600 hp.
Cost: $13,000

PERFORMANCE

Maximum speed: 204 mph.
Cruising speed: 167 mph.
Range: 480 miles
Service ceiling: 24,400 ft.

CLASSIC FIGHTERS

SOPWITH F–1 "CAMEL"

The Sopwith Camel was the most successful fighter plane of WW I. It shot down more enemy aircraft than any other fighter of any of the warring nations. However, because of its tricky handling characteristics, more men lost their lives while learning to fly it than died while using it in combat. The Camel was produced in Great Britain and went into action in July 1917 with the Royal Flying Corps.

Two U.S. Air Service squadrons, the 17th and 148th, used the Camel in combat while assigned to British forces during the summer and fall of 1918. A third U.S. unit, the 185th Aero Squadron, used the Camel as a night fighter.

Although 5,490 Camels were produced, very few remain in existence today. The Camel on display was built by U.S. Air Force personnel from original WW I factory drawings and was completed in 1974. It is painted and marked as the Camel flown by Lt. George A. Vaughn, Jr., 17th Aero Squadron.

SPECIFICATIONS

Span: 28 ft. 0 in.
Height: 8 ft 6 in.
Armament: Two Vickers .303–cal. machine guns
Engine: Clerget rotary of 130 hp.

Length: 18 ft. 9 in.
Weight: 1,482 lbs. maximum

PERFORMANCE

Maximum speed: 112 mph.
Range: 300 miles
Service ceiling: 21,000 ft.

CLASSIC FIGHTERS

BOEING P–12E

The P–12 was one of the most successful American fighters produced between WW I and WW II. Used by both the Army and Navy (as the F4B), the P–12 was developed from prototypes built by the Boeing Airplane Company at their own expense. It was produced in a basic version and five additional series, B through F. The basic P–12 and the B, C and D series had fabric–covered fuselages of bolted aluminum tubing. P–12E and F fuselages were of all–metal, semimonocoque (stressed skin) construction. All had wooden wings with fabric covering. The Army Air Corps received its first P–12 in February 1929, and the last P–12F in May 1932. The last of the biplane fighters flown by the Army; some remained in service until 1941. In all, 366 were produced.

The P–12E on display served with the 6th Pursuit Squadron in Hawaii during the 1930s and was retired in 1940. It was donated to the USAF Museum in 1973 by Marcellus Foose and Glen Courtwright of Oaklawn, Illinois. Museum specialists began restoration in 1974 and completed it in 1983.

SPECIFICATIONS

Span: 30 ft. **Length:** 20 ft. 4 in. **Height:** 9 ft.
Weight: 2,690 lbs. loaded
Armament: Two .30–cal. machine guns or one .30–cal. and one .50–cal.; 244 lbs. of bombs carried externally

Engine: Pratt & Whitney R–1340–17 of 500 hp.
Crew: One
Cost: $15,000

PERFORMANCE

Maximum speed: 189 mph.
Cruising speed: 160 mph.
Range: 570 miles
Service ceiling: 26,300 ft.

CLASSIC FIGHTERS

LOCKHEED P–38L "LIGHTNING"

The Lightning was designed in 1937 as a high–altitude interceptor. The first one built, the XP–38, made its public debut on February 11, 1939, by flying from California to New York in seven hours. Because of its unorthodox design, the airplane experienced "growing pains" and it required several years to perfect it for combat. Late in 1942, it went into large–scale operations during the North African campaign where the German Luftwaffe named it "Der Gabel-schwanz Teufel"—"The Forked-Tail Devil."

Equipped with droppable fuel tanks under its wings, the P–38 was used extensively as a long–range escort fighter and saw action in practically every major combat area of the world. A very versatile aircraft, the Lightning was also used for dive bombing, level bombing, ground strafing and photo reconnaissance missions.

By the end of production in 1945, 9,923 P–38s had been built. The P–38L on display, painted as a P–38J with the 55th Fighter Squadron based in England, was donated to the Museum in 1961 by the Bob Bean Aircraft Corp., Hawthorne, California, and the Kaufmann Foundation, Philadelphia.

SPECIFICATIONS

Span: 52 ft. **Length:** 37 ft. 10 in. **Height:** 12 ft. 10 in. **Weight:** 17,500 lbs. loaded
Armament: Four .50–cal. machine guns and one 20mm cannon   **Cost:** $115,000
Engines: Two Allison V–1710s of 1,475 hp. ea.

PERFORMANCE

Maximum speed: 414 mph.
Cruising speed: 275 mph.
Range: 1,100 miles
Service ceiling: 40,000 ft.

CLASSIC FIGHTERS

CURTISS P–40E "WARHAWK"

The P–40, developed from the P–36, was America's foremost fighter in service when WW II began. P–40s engaged Japanese aircraft during the attack on Pearl Harbor and the invasion of the Philippines in December 1941. They also were flown in China early in 1942 by the famed Flying Tigers and in North Africa in 1943 by the first AAF all–black unit, the 99th Fighter Squadron.

The P–40 served in numerous combat areas: the Aleutian Islands, North Africa, Italy, the Far East, the Southwest Pacific and some were sent to Russia. Though often outclassed by its adversaries in speed, maneuverability and rate of climb, the P–40 earned a reputation in battle for extreme ruggedness. At the end of the P–40's brilliant career, more than 14,000 had been produced for service in the air forces of 28 nations, of which 2,320 were of the "E" series.

The airplane on display, a "Kittyhawk" (the export version of the P–40E built for the RAF), was obtained from Mr. Charles P. Doyle, Rosemount, Minnesota.

SPECIFICATIONS

Span: 37 ft. 4 in.   **Length:** 31 ft. 9 in.   **Height:** 12 ft. 4 in.   **Weight:** 9,100 lbs. loaded
Armament: Six .50–cal. machine guns; 700 lbs. of bombs externally
Engine: Allison V–1710 of 1,150 hp.   **Cost:** $45,000

PERFORMANCE

Maximum speed: 362 mph.
Cruising speed: 235 mph.
Range: 850 miles   **Ceiling:** 30,000 ft.

CLASSIC FIGHTERS

REPUBLIC P–47D "THUNDERBOLT"

Affectionately nicknamed "Jug," the P–47 was one of the most famous AAF fighter planes of WW II. Although originally conceived as a lightweight interceptor, the P–47 was developed as a heavyweight fighter and made its first flight on May 6, 1941. The first production model was delivered to the AAF in March 1942, and in April 1943 the Thunderbolt flew its first combat mission—a sweep over Western Europe. Used as both a high–altitude escort fighter and a low–level fighter–bomber, the P–47 quickly gained a reputation for ruggedness. Its sturdy construction and air–cooled radial engine enabled the Thunderbolt to absorb severe battle damage and keep on flying. During WW II, the P–47 served in almost every active war theater and in the air forces of several Allied nations. By the end of WW II, more than 15,600 Thunderbolts had been built.

The aircraft on display was acquired by the Museum in 1981. It is marked as a –D with the 1st Air Commando Group in China in 1944–5.

SPECIFICATIONS

Span: 40 ft. 9 in.   **Length:** 36 ft. 2 in.   **Crew:** One
Height: 14 ft. 8 in.   **Weight:** 17,500 lbs. max.   **Cost:** $85,000
Armament: Six or Eight .50–cal. machine guns and either ten rockets or 2,500 lbs. of bombs   **Engine:** One Pratt & Whitney R–2800–59 of 2,430 hp.

PERFORMANCE

Maximum speed: 433 mph.
Cruising speed: 350 mph.
Range: 1,030 miles
Service ceiling: 42,000 ft.

CLASSIC FIGHTERS

NORTH AMERICAN P–51D "MUSTANG"

The P-51 was designed as the NA–73 in 1940 at Britain's request. The design showed promise and AAF purchases of Allison–powered Mustangs began in 1941 primarily for photo recon and ground support use due to its limited high–altitude performance. But in 1942, tests of P-51s using the British Rolls-Royce "Merlin" engine revealed much improved speed and service ceiling, and in December 1943, Merlin-powered P-51Bs first entered combat over Europe. Providing high–altitude escort to B-17s and B-24s, they scored heavily over German interceptors and by war's end, P-51s had destroyed 4,950 enemy aircraft in the air, more than any other AAF fighter in Europe.

The P-51D on display was obtained from the West Virginia ANG in 1957 and was the last prop–driven USAF fighter assigned to a tactical unit. It is painted as the D model flown by Col. C. L. Sluder, CO of the 325th Fighter Group, 15th AF, in Italy in 1944.

SPECIFICATIONS

Span: 37 ft. 0 in.   **Length:** 32 ft. 3 in.   **Cost:** $54,000
Height: 13 ft. 8 in.   **Weight:** 12,100 lbs. max.
Armament: Six .50–cal. machine guns and ten 5 in. rockets or 2,000 lbs. of bombs
Engine: Packard built Rolls–Royce "Merlin" V–1650 of 1,695 hp.

PERFORMANCE

Maximum speed: 437 mph.
Cruising speed: 275 mph.
Range: 1,000 miles
Service ceiling: 41,900 ft.

CLASSIC FIGHTERS

SUPERMARINE SPITFIRE MK XI

The Mark XI was a development of the original British Spitfire interceptor that first flew in 1936. The Mark XI was essentially a Mark IX Spitfire modified for photographic reconnaissance with cameras and a more powerful engine. All guns and armor were removed and the fuel capacity was greatly increased. Speed was the unarmed Mark XI's defense. A total of 471 Mark XIs were built between April 1943 and January 1946. Various photo-reconnaissance versions of the Spitfire were built and used by Great Britain and her allies with great success in all theaters during World War II. A total of 20,351 Spitfires of all types were eventually built, plus 2,408 Seafires modified to operate from aircraft carriers.

The USAAF's 14th Photographic Squadron of the 8th Air Force used Spitfire Mark XIs from November 1943 to April 1945, flying hazardous long range reconnaissance missions. This aircraft is painted and marked as a Mark XI that served with the 14th at Mount Farm airfield in England It was placed on display in May 1993.

SPECIFICATIONS
Span: 36 ft. 10 in. **Length:** 30 ft.
Height: 12 ft. 7 in. **Weight:** 8,040 lbs. loaded
Engine: One liquid-cooled Rolls-Royce Merlin 61, 63, or 70 of 1,655 hp..

PERFORMANCE
Maximum speed: 422 mph
Cruising speed: 369 mph
Range: 1,360
Service ceiling: 37,000 ft.

CLASSIC FIGHTERS

MESSERSCHMITT Bf 109G-10

The Messerschmitt Bf 109 began as an entry by the Bayerische Flugzeugwerke in a Luftwaffe (German Air Force) fighter competition in the early 1930s. Willy Messerschmitt's creation represented one of the most advanced aerodynamic designs at the time, with retractable landing gear, an enclosed cockpit, automatic leading edge slats, cantilever wings, and stressed skin construction. During the trials, the Bf 109 clearly outperformed the larger and heavier favorite Heinkel He 112. The first production models began coming off the lines in 1936. The redesignation of the Bayerische Flugzeugwerke AG to Messerschmitt AG in 1938 led many to call it the Me 109, although the official Luftwaffe designation of the aircraft remained the Bf 109 throughout the war.

This Bf 109G-10 is painted to represent an aircraft from Jagdgeschwader 300, a unit that defended Germany against Allied bombers.

SPECIFICATIONS

Span: 32 ft. 6.5 in.   **Length:** 29 ft. .5 in.
Height: 8 ft. 2.5 in.   **Weight:** 5,800 lbs.
Armament: One 30mm MK 108 cannon and two 13mm MG131 machine guns
Engine: One Daimler–Benz DB 605D of 1,852 hp.

PERFORMANCE

Maximum speed: 426 mph.
Range: 373 miles
Service ceiling: 41,400 ft.

CLASSIC FIGHTERS

NORTH AMERICAN F–86A "SABRE"

The F–86, the USAF's first swept–wing jet fighter, made its initial flight on October 1, 1947. The first production model flew on May 20, 1948, and on September 15, 1948, an F–86A set a new world speed record of 670.9 mph. Originally designed as a high–altitude day fighter, it was subsequently redesigned into an all–weather interceptor (F–86D) and a fighter-bomber (F–86H). As a day fighter, the airplane saw service in Korea in three successive series (F–86A, E, and F) where it engaged the Russian–built MiG–15. By the end of hostilities, it had shot down 792 MiGs at a loss of only 76 Sabres, a victory ratio of 10 to 1.

More than 5,500 Sabre day–fighters were built in the U.S. and Canada. The airplane was also used by the air forces of 20 other nations, including West Germany, Japan, Spain, Britain and Australia.

The F–86A on display was flown to the USAF Museum in 1961. It is marked as the 4th Fighter Group F–86A flown by Lt. Col. Bruce Hinton on Dec. 17, 1950 when he became the first F–86 pilot to shoot down a MiG.

SPECIFICATIONS

Span: 37 ft. 1 in. **Length:** 37 ft. 6 in. **Engine:** General Electric J47
Cost: $178,000 **Height:** 14 ft. 8 in. **Weight:** 13,791 lbs. loaded
Armament: Six .50–cal. machine guns and eight 5 in. rockets or 2,000 lbs. of bombs

PERFORMANCE

Maximum speed: 685 mph.
Cruising speed: 540 mph.
Range: 1,200 miles **Ceiling:** 49,000 ft.

CLASSIC FIGHTERS

McDONNELL DOUGLAS F–4C "PHANTOM II"

First flown in May 1958, the Phantom II originally was developed for U.S. Navy fleet defense and entered service in 1961. The USAF evaluated it for close air support, interdiction and counter–air operations and, in 1962, approved a USAF version. The USAF's Phantom II, designated F–4C, made its first flight on May 27, 1963. Production deliveries began in November 1963. In its air–to–ground role the F–4 could carry twice the normal bomb load of a WW II B–17. USAF F–4s also flew reconnaissance and "Wild Weasel" anti–aircraft missile suppression missions. Phantom II production ended in 1979 after over 5,000 had been built—more than 2,600 for the USAF.

In 1965 the first USAF Phantom IIs were sent to Southeast Asia (SEA). The first USAF pilot to score four combat victories with F–4s in SEA was Colonel Robin Olds, a WW II ace.

The aircraft on display is the one in which Colonel Olds, as commander, and Lieutenant Stephen B. Crocker, the backseat pilot, scored two of those victories in a single day, May 20, 1967.

SPECIFICATIONS
Span: 38 ft. 5 in.   **Length:** 58 ft. 2 in.   **Height:** 16 ft. 6 in.   **Weight:** 58,000 lbs. loaded
Armament: Up to 16,000 lbs. of nuclear or conventional bombs, rockets, missiles, cannon pods
Engines: Two General Electric J–79–GE–15s of 17,000 lbs. thrust each w/afterburner
Crew: Two **Cost:** $1,900,000

PERFORMANCE
Maximum speed: 1,400 mph.
Cruising speed: 590 mph.
Range: 1,750 miles
Service ceiling: 59,600 ft.

CLASSIC FIGHTERS

McDONNELL DOUGLAS F–15A "EAGLE"

The F–15 is a twin engine, high performance, all–weather air superiority fighter. First flown on July 27, 1972, the Eagle entered USAF inventory on November 14, 1974. It was the first U.S. fighter to have engine thrust greater than the normal weight of the aircraft, allowing it to accelerate while in a vertical climb. The Eagle has been produced in single–seat and two–seat versions. During Operation Desert Storm, F–15Cs conducted counter-air operations over Iraq. They escorted strike aircraft over long distances and scored 30 aerial victories during the conflict. The F-15E was used to search out and attack "Scud" ballistic missile launchers.

In 1980 this F-15A, 76-027, was delivered to the 27th Tactical Fighter Squadron, 1st Tactical Fighter Wing, at Langley AFB, Virginia, and is painted in the colors of that squadron.

SPECIFICATIONS
Span: 42 ft. 9 3/4 in.
Length: 63 ft. 9 in.
Height: 18 in. 7 1/2 in.
Weight: 56,000 lbs. max.,
Cost: $10,890,000.

Armament: One M–61A1 20mm Vulcan cannon, 4 AIM–7 Sparrow, and 4 AIM–9 Sidewinder missiles, plus 15,000 lbs. mixed ordnance carried externally.

Engines: Two Pratt & Whitney F100–PW–100 turbofans of 25,000 lbs. thrust each.

PERFORMANCE
Maximum speed: 1,600 mph+
Range: 3,450 miles with external fuel tanks.
Service ceiling: 65,000 ft.

CLASSIC FIGHTERS

GENERAL DYNAMICS F–16A "FIGHTING FALCON"

The F-16 evolved from a 1972 USAF lightweight fighter prototype program which sought a small, lightweight, low cost, air superiority day fighter designed for high performance and ease of maintenance. It achieved combat-ready status in October 1980. Many foreign nations have purchased the fighter.

The F-16A on display was one of the first F-16s to be received by the "Thunderbirds" Aerial Demonstration Team in 1982 when they transitioned from T-38s to F-16s. The Thunderbirds continued to fly this aircraft until 1992 when they converted to F-16Cs. It was then modified back to operational configuration and assigned to the Air Education and Training Command to train pilots at Luke AFB, Arizona. In 1996 the Thunderbirds repainted it in its Thunderbird colors at Nellis AFB, Nevada. The Museum placed it on display in September 1996.

SPECIFICATIONS

Span: 32 ft. 10 in. **Length:** 49 ft. 6 in.
Height: 16 ft. 5 in. **Weight:** 29,896 lbs. loaded
Armament: One 20mm M–61A1 cannon and various combinations of air–to–air and air–to–ground missiles and bombs.

Engine: One Pratt & Whitney F100–PW–200 of 23,830 lbs. thrust with afterburner
Crew: One
Cost: $8,200,000

PERFORMANCE

Maximum speed: 1,345 mph.
Cruising speed: 577 mph.
Range: 1,407 miles
Service ceiling: 55,000 ft.

CLASSIC TRAINERS

STEARMAN PT–13D "KAYDET"

The PT–13 was typical of the biplane primary trainers used during the late 1930s and WW II. Whereas it was powered by a Lycoming engine, the same airplane with a Continental engine was designated the PT–17, and with a Jacobs engine, the PT–18. A later version which featured a cockpit canopy was designated the PT–27.

Of 10,346 Kaydets ordered for the U.S. and its Allies, 4,360 of these went to the Army Air Force. Following WW II, the Kaydet was phased out in favor of more modern trainers.

The PT–13D on display, donated in 1959 by the Boeing Airplane Company (which purchased the Stearman Company in 1938), was the last Kaydet produced.

SPECIFICATIONS

Span: 32 ft. 2 in.
Height: 9 ft. 2 in.
Armament: None
Engine: Lycoming R–680 of 220 hp.

Length: 24 ft. 10 in.
Weight: 2,717 lbs. loaded

Cost: $11,000

PERFORMANCE

Maximum speed: 125 mph.
Cruising speed: 104 mph.
Range: 450 miles
Service ceiling: 14,000 ft.

CLASSIC TRAINERS

BEECHCRAFT AT-10

In 1940-41, the Beech Aircraft Company designed an advanced multi-engine trainer for ease and speed of manufacture on a large scale and named it the "Wichita." To conserve scarce metals needed for combat aircraft, Beech built the airframe out of plywood with only the engine cowlings and cockpit enclosure constructed of aluminum. The fuel tanks also were made of wood and covered with neoprene, a synthetic rubber. The extensive use of wood permitted Beech to subcontract the production of many components to furniture makers and other firms. This advanced trainer, designated the AT-10, had superior performance among twin engine trainers of its type and over half of the Army Air Force's pilots received transitional training from single- to multi-engine aircraft in them. Between 1941 and 1943, Beech built 1,771 AT-10s and Globe Aircraft Corporation (which become Temco after World War II) built 600 in Dallas, Texas. The Air Force Museum's AT-10 was placed on display in June 1997.

SPECIFICATIONS

Span: 44 ft.   **Length:** 34 ft. 4 in.
Height: 10 ft. 4 in. **Weight:** 6,465 lbs.
Engine: Two 295 hp Lycoming R-680-9 radial engines

PERFORMANCE

Maximum speed: 190 mph.
Range: 660 miles
Ceiling: Approx. 20,000 ft.

CLASSIC TRAINERS

NORTH AMERICAN T–6D "MOSQUITO"

The T-6, originally known as the Texan, was the sole single-engine advanced trainer for the USAAF (U.S. Army Air Forces) during WWII, and 15,495 were built between 1938 and 1945. The T-6 continued to train pilots in the newly formed USAF.

During the Korean War, airborne forward air controllers (FACs) chose the T-6 as the best available aircraft because it could operate from small, rough airstrips and was easy to maintain. More importantly, the T-6 was faster and more rugged than the light liaison aircraft they initially flew. Even though this WWII trainer was not designed to fly in combat, it performed well in its role as an airborne FAC, where it became known as the "Mosquito."

The T-6D on display flew as an early Mosquito with the 6147th Tactical Air Control Group during the first two years of the Korean War. The USAF Museum acquired it in 1995.

SPECIFICATIONS
Span: 42 ft.   **Length:** 29 ft. 6 in.
Height: 10 ft. 10 in. **Weight:** 5,617 lbs. loaded
Engine: Pratt & Whitney   R–1340 of 600 hp. **Cost:** $27,000

PERFORMANCE
Maximum speed: 206 mph.
Cruising speed: 145 mph.
Range: 1,000 miles with drop tank
Service ceiling: 23,200 ft.

CLASSIC TRAINERS

LOCKHEED T–33A "SHOOTING STAR"

The two-place T-33 jet was designed for training pilots already qualified to fly propeller-driven aircraft. It was developed from the single-seat F-80 fighter by lengthening the fuselage slightly more than three feet to accommodate a second cockpit.

Originally designated the TF-80C, the T-33 made its first flight in March 1948. Production continued until August 1959 with 5,691 T-33s built. In addition to its use as a trainer, the T-33 has been used for such tasks as drone director and target towing, and in some countries even as a combat aircraft. The RT-33A reconnaissance version, produced primarily for use by foreign countries, had a camera installed in the nose and additional equipment in the rear cockpit.

The T-33 is one of the world's best known aircraft, having served with the air forces of more than 20 different countries for over 40 years. Some are still in use throughout the world. The T-33A on display was flown to the museum in 1962.

SPECIFICATIONS

Span: 37 ft. 6 in.	**Length:** 37 ft. 8 in.	**Engine:** Allison J–33 of
Height: 11 ft. 7 in.	**Weight:** 15,000 lbs. max.	5,400 lbs. thrust
Armament: Two .50-cal. machine guns in nose		**Cost:** $123,000

PERFORMANCE

Maximum speed: 525 mph.
Cruising speed: 455 mph.
Range: 1,000 miles
Service ceiling: 45,000 ft.

SPECIFICATIONS

Span: 27 ft. 11 1/2 in.
Length: 23 ft. 10 in.
Height: 10 ft. 5 in.
Weight: 2,955 lbs. loaded
Armament: Two fixed .30 caliber machine guns or one .50 and one .30 caliber machine gun. Up to 200 lbs of bombs.
Engine: Pratt & Whitney R1340-27 of 500 hp.
Cost: $16,567

PERFORMANCE

Maximum speed: 234 mph.
Cruising speed: 199 mph.
Range: 360 miles
Service ceiling: 27,400 ft.

BOEING P-26A

The P-26A, affectionately called the "Peashooter" by its pilots, was the first all-metal, monoplane fighter produced for the U.S. Army Air Corps. It was the last Army Air Corps aircraft accepted with an open cockpit, a fixed undercarriage, and an externally braced wing. Significantly faster in level flight than previous fighters, the P-26A's relatively high landing speed caused the introduction of landing flaps to reduce this speed.

Boeing initially designed the P-26 in 1931, designating it first as Model 248 and in December 1931 as the XP-936. The first flight occurred on March 20, 1932. The Army Air Corps purchased the three prototypes and designated them as P-26s. The Air Corps purchased a total of 111 of the production version, designated P-26A, and 25 of later B and C models.

The P-26 was the Army Air Corps' frontline fighter before it was replaced during 1938-40 by the Curtiss P-36A and the Seversky P-35.

This P-26A reproduction is painted to represent the commander's aircraft of the 19th Pursuit Squadron, 18th Pursuit Group, stationed at Wheeler Field, Hawaii, in 1938.

MARTIN B-10

The B-10, the first of the "modern-day" all-metal monoplane bombers to be produced in quantity, featured such innovations as internal bomb storage, retractable landing gear, a rotating gun turret, and enclosed cockpits. It was so advanced in design that it was 50 percent faster than contemporary biplane bombers and as fast as most of the fighters. When the Air Corps ordered 121 B-10s in the 1933–36 period, it was the largest procurement of bomber aircraft since WW I. It also ordered 32 B-10 type bombers with Pratt and Whitney rather than Wright engines and designated these as B-12s.

General Henry H. "Hap" Arnold once called the B-10 the air power wonder of its day. In 1934 he led ten B-10s on a 7,360 mile flight from Washington, D.C., to Fairbanks, Alaska, and back. Although Air Corps B-10s and B-12s were replaced by B-17s and B-18s in the late 1930s, China and the Netherlands flew export versions in combat against Japan.

The aircraft on display is painted as a B-10 used in the 1934 Alaskan Flight. The only known remaining B-10, it was an export version sold to Argentina in 1938. Donated by the Government of Argentina to the U.S. Government for the Air Force Museum in 1971, it was restored by the 96th Maintenance Squadron (Mobile), Air Force Reserve, at Kelly AFB, Texas, in 1973–76.

SPECIFICATIONS

Span: 70 ft. 6 in.
Length: 44 ft. 9 in.
Height: 15 ft. 5 in.
Weight: 14,700 lbs. loaded
Armament: Three .30 cal. machine guns, 2,200 lbs. of bombs
Engines: Two Wright R-1820's of 775 hp. ea.
Cost: $55,000

PERFORMANCE

Maximum speed: 215 mph.
Cruising speed: 183 mph.
Range: 1,370 miles
Service ceiling: 24,000 ft.

SPECIFICATIONS

Span: 40 ft. 0 in.
Length: 32 ft. 0 in.
Height: 13 ft 6 in.
Weight: 5,401 lbs. max.
Armament: None on O–38Fs
(other O–38s carried two .30–cal.
machine guns, one fixed
forward–firing and one flexible)
Engine: Pratt & Whitney R–1690
of 625 hp.
Cost: $12,000

PERFORMANCE

Maximum speed: 152 mph.
Cruising speed: 128 mph.
Range: 700 miles
Service ceiling: 19,750 ft.

DOUGLAS O–38F

The role of the observation plane has often been overshadowed by the exploits of bombers and fighters, but aerial reconnaissance has always been one of the most fundamental missions of military aviation.

One of the best–known Air Corps observation planes of the 1930s was the O-38. Between 1931 and 1934, Douglas built 156 O–38s for the Air Corps, eight of which were O–38Fs. Some were still in service at the time of Pearl Harbor in 1941.

The O–38F on display was one of the first military aircraft assigned to Alaska. In October 1940 it became the first airplane to land at Ladd Field near Fairbanks, Alaska, the Air Corps' new cold–weather test station. This plane flew various missions in that area until it made a crash landing in the wilderness 70 miles southeast of Fairbanks in June 1941 due to engine failure. The pilot, Lt. Milton H. Ashkins, and mechanic, Sgt. R. A. Roberts, were uninjured and hiked to safety after supplies were dropped to them. The aircraft remained abandoned until the U.S. Air Force Museum learned of its existence and arranged for its recovery. It was lifted from the crash site by helicopter in June 1968, and despite exposure to the weather for 27 years, it was remarkably well–preserved. Museum personnel completed its restoration in 1974.

CURTISS O–52 "OWL"

In 1940, the Air Corps ordered 203 Curtiss O–52s for observation duties. Upon delivery, the airplane was used in military maneuvers within the USA, but following America's entry into WW II, the AAF determined that the airplane did not possess sufficient performance for "modern" combat operations in overseas areas. As a result, the O–52 was relegated to courier duties within the USA and short–range submarine patrols over the Gulf of Mexico and the Atlantic and Pacific Oceans.

The O–52 was the last "O" type airplane procured in quantity for the Air Corps. Following the attack on Pearl Harbor, the "O" designation was cancelled and "L" for liaison type airplanes was adopted to replace it.

The airplane on display was obtained from the U.S. Federal Reformatory at Chillicothe, Ohio, in November 1962. It was restored by the Pittsburgh Institute of Aeronautics, Pittsburgh, Pennsylvania.

SPECIFICATIONS
Span: 40 ft. 9 1/2 in.
Length: 26 ft. 4 3/4 in.
Height: 9 ft. 11 1/2 in.
Weight: 5,364 lbs. loaded
Armament: One forward and one rearward firing .30–cal. machine guns
Engine: Pratt & Whitney R–1340–51 of 600 hp.

PERFORMANCE
Maximum speed: 215 mph.
Cruising speed: 169 mph.
Range: 455 miles
Service ceiling: 23,200 ft.
Cost: $31,000

SPECIFICATIONS

Span: 47 ft. 9 in.
Length: 31 ft. 8 in.
Height: 9 ft. 3 in.
Weight: 7,543 lbs. loaded
Armament: Four fixed and one flexible mount .30 caliber machine guns and up to 1,100 lbs. of bombs
Engine: One Pratt & Whitney R-1535-B of 825 hp.
Crew: Two
Cost: $26,000

PERFORMANCE

Maximum speed: 220 mph.
Cruising speed: 170 mph.
Range: 732 miles
Service ceiling: 19,400 ft.

NORTHROP A-17A

The A-17 series was a direct descendent of the pace setting Northrop "Gamma" made famous by the aerial explorer Lincoln Ellsworth. It replaced the Curtiss A-8 and A-12 "Shrike" and was the last of the pre-war single-engine attack aircraft ordered into production by the Army Air Corps.

Caught in the pre-World War II doctrine that emphasized air superiority over ground support, the A-17 was never fully tested in peacetime exercises or in combat. Its fate was sealed in 1938 when the Army Air Corps determined that all future attack aircraft procured would be multi-engine models.

Despite this handicap, the A-17's design and novel features, such as the split perforated flaps, figured prominently in the success of a distinguished line of Douglas aircraft including the "Dauntless" dive bomber and the post World War II "Skyraider."

The first 109 production A-17s featured fixed partially enclosed landing gear. One hundred and twenty-nine A-17As configured with fully retractable landing gear and a more powerful engine followed between February 1937 and August 1938.

The aircraft on display is the only A-17 series aircraft known to exist. It was delivered to the Air Corps and assigned to Barksdale Field, Louisiana, on 25 June 1937.

DOUGLAS B–18A "BOLO"

The Douglas Aircraft Co. developed the B–18 to replace the Martin B–10 as the Army Air Corps' standard bomber. The Bolo's design was based on the Douglas DC–2 commercial transport. During Air Corps bomber trials at Wright Field in 1935, the B–18 prototype competed with the Martin 146 (an improved B–10) and the four engine Boeing 299, forerunner of the B–17. Although many Air Corps officers believed the Boeing design was superior, only 13 YB–17s were initially ordered. Instead, the Army General Staff selected the less costly Bolo and, in January 1936, ordered 133 as B–18s. Later, 217 more were built as B–18As with a "shark" nose in which the bombardier's position was extended forward over the nose gunner's station, as displayed here.

By 1939, underpowered and with inadequate defensive armament, the Bolo was the Air Corps' primary bomber. Some B–18s were destroyed by the Japanese on December 7, 1941. By early 1942, improved aircraft replaced the Bolo as a first–line bombardment aircraft. Many B–18s were then used as transports, or modified as B–18Bs for anti-submarine duty. The B–18A on display was stationed at Wright Field from 1939 to 1942. The Museum acquired it in 1971 and restored it as a B–18A serving in 1939 with the 38th Reconnaissance Squadron.

SPECIFICATIONS

Span: 89 ft. 6 in.
Length: 57 ft. 10 in.
Height: 15 ft. 2 in.
Weight: 27,000 lbs. loaded
Armament: Three .30–cal. guns (in nose, ventral, and dorsal positions), plus 4,500 lbs. of bombs carried internally
Engines: Two Wright R–1820-53s of 1,000 hp. ea.
Crew: Six
Cost: $80,000

PERFORMANCE

Maximum speed: 215 mph. at 15,000 ft.
Cruising speed: 167 mph.
Range: 2,100 miles
Service ceiling: 23,900 ft.

SPECIFICATIONS

Span: 36 ft. 0 in.
Length: 25 ft. 4 in.
Height: 9 ft. 9 1/2 in.
Weight: 5,600 lbs. max.
Armament: One .50–cal. and one .30–cal. fuselage–mounted machine gun plus 320 lbs. of bombs.
Engine: Pratt & Whitney R–1830 of 850 hp.
Crew: One
Cost: $22,500

PERFORMANCE

Maximum speed: 280 mph.
Cruising speed: 260 mph.
Range: 625 miles
Service ceilng: 30,600 ft.

SEVERSKY P–35

The P–35, one of the forerunners of the Republic P–47, was the first single-seat, all–metal pursuit plane with retractable landing gear and enclosed cockpit to go into regular service with the U. S. Army Air Corps. The Army accepted 76 P–35s in 1937-38 and assigned 75 to the 1st Pursuit Group Selfridge Field, Michigan.

The Japanese Navy ordered 20 of a two–seat version of the P–35 in 1938, the only American–built planes used operationally by a Japanese squadron during WW II. Sweden also purchased 60 improved single–seat EP–106s, but a second order for 60 was taken over by the U. S. Army in 1940 and designated P–35As. Most were assigned to the 17th and 20th Pursuit Squadrons in the Philippines; all were lost in action early in the war.

The aircraft on display served with the 94th Pursuit Squadron at Selfridge Field. It was restored by maintenance personnel of the 133rd Tactical Airlift Wing, Minnesota ANG, with assistance from students of the Minneapolis Vocational Institute.

CURTISS P–36A "HAWK"

The P–36, developed from the Curtiss "Hawk" Model 75, was the direct forerunner of the famed P-40. Production deliveries to the Air Corps began in 1938 and eventually the Army acquired 243 P-36s, including 30 undelivered Norwegian P-36s acquired by the U.S. in 1942 after Germany occupied Norway.

France used the Hawk 75A in combat over Europe in 1939 and 1940, even though the airplane was obsolete when compared to its major adversary, the Messerschmitt Bf 109. In 1941, the Army Air Corps transferred 39 of its P-36s to Hawaii and 20 to Alaska. When the Japanese attacked Pearl Harbor, two of the first six Army Air Forces fighters to get off the ground were P-36s. One of the P-36s was flown by Lt Philip M. Rasmussen who downed a Japanese aircraft. With the outbreak of hostilities, the outmoded P-36 was relegated to training and courier duties within the U.S. Many of the P-36s were sent to other countries through Lend Lease.

The airplane on display at the Air Force Museum is marked to represent Lt Rasmussen's P-36A, s/n 38-86 as it appeared on December 7, 1941, at Pearl Harbor. The aircraft was donated by Mr and Mrs Edward S. Perkins, Sr., of Anniston, Alabama, in April 1959.

SPECIFICATIONS

Span: 37 ft. 4 in.
Length: 28 ft. 6 in.
Height: 8 ft. 5 in.
Weight: 5,650 lbs. loaded
Armament: Two .30–cal. or two .50–cal. machine guns
Engine: Pratt & Whitney R–1830 of 1,050 hp.
Cost: $23,000

PERFORMANCE

Maximum speed: 313 mph.
Cruising speed: 250 mph.
Range: 830 miles
Service ceiling: 32,700 ft.

SPECIFICATIONS

Span: 85 ft. 0 in.
Length: 61 ft. 9 in.
Height: 16 ft. 1 in.
Weight: 21,000 lbs. maximum
Armament: None
Engines: Two Wright R–1820s of 975 hp. ea.
Cost: $73,000

PERFORMANCE

Maximum speed: 210 mph.
Cruising speed: 155 mph.
Range: 900 miles.
Service ceiling: 20,600 ft.

DOUGLAS C–39A

The C–39 transport, forerunner of the world–famous C–47, was a composite of Douglas military and civilian aircraft designs. The fuselage was copied from the DC–2 commercial airliner (Air Corps designation, C–33), the tail was almost identical to that of the DC–3 airliner, and the landing gear was based on that of the Douglas B–18 bomber.

Douglas built 35 C–39As and delivered them to the Air Corps in 1939. These aircraft were called upon to perform many rigorous transport duties early in WW II, including the evacuation of personnel from the Philippines to Australia in December 1941. Also, it was a C–39A that blazed the trail from Maine to Gander, Newfoundland, in January 1942, the first leg of the aerial lifeline to Great Britain.

The C-39A on display was donated to the U.S. Air Force Museum in July 1970. During its service life, it was based at Wright–Patterson AFB between 1939 and 1942.

BEECH UC–43 "TRAVELER"

One of the most distinctive WW II USAAF aircraft was the UC–43 "Traveler," a light transport biplane with negative or backward staggered wings. Three examples of the popular Beech commercial Model 17 "Staggerwing" aircraft, delivered in June 1939 for Army evaluation, were designated YC–43s. These were assigned to the U.S. air attaches at the American Embassies in London, Paris, and Rome in 1939 and were operated by U.S. Army Air Corps personnel.

Early in WW II, the need for a compact executive–type transport or courier aircraft became apparent, and in 1942 the Army ordered the first of 270 Model 17s for service in this country and overseas as UC–43s. These differed only in minor details from the commercial model. To meet urgent wartime needs, the government also purchased or leased additional "Staggerwings" from private owners including 118 more for the USAAF plus others for the Navy.

The aircraft on display, donated by Major Richard River, USAF (Ret) of Chillicothe, Ohio, was flown to the Museum in May, 1974. It was procured by the Army during WW II but was assigned to the Navy as a GB–2. It is painted and marked as a UC–43 assigned to the 8th AF in England in 1943 as a liaison aircraft.

SPECIFICATIONS
Span: 32 ft.
Length: 26 ft. 1 1/2 in.
Height: 8 ft.
Weight: 4,250 lbs. maximum
Armament: None
Engine: Pratt & Whitney
R–985 of 450 hp.
Cost: $19,000

PERFORMANCE
Maximum speed: 212 mph.
Cruising speed: 202 mph.
Range: 785 miles
Service ceiling: 20,000 ft.

SPECIFICATIONS

Span: 40 ft.
Length: 31 ft. 4 in.
Height: 13 ft.
Weight: 7,200 lbs. loaded
Armament: Eight .303–cal.
Browning machine guns
Engine: Rolls–Royce Merlin XX
of 1,260 hp.
Crew: One

PERFORMANCE

Maximum speed: 340 mph.
Cruising speed: 238 mph.
Range: 468 miles with internal
fuel only; 1,090 miles with two
90 gal. ferry tanks
Service ceiling: 35,000 ft.

HAWKER HURRICANE MKIIA

The Hawker Hurricane was one of the most famous British fighters of WW II. The prototype was first flown in November 1935, and the first production aircraft made its initial flight in October 1937. Within a matter of weeks, Hurricanes were being delivered to their operational squadrons. By the time war broke out in September 1939, the Royal Air Force (RAF) had taken delivery of about 500 Hurricanes as production continued.

The Hurricane is probably best known for its performance during the Battle of Britain. When the battle commenced in July 1940, the RAF Fighter Command had but 527 Hurricanes and 321 Spitfires to counter the enemy's 2,700 aircraft. Yet, the RAF was able to maintain air superiority in the skies of Great Britain.

Hurricanes were built not only in Great Britain but also in Yugoslavia, before the German invasion, and in Canada during the 1940–1942 period. They were flown by pilots of many nations during the war. The Hawker Hurricane MK IIA on display is a Canadian built airframe painted to represent an aircraft of 71 Squadron, Royal Air Force, one of the three Eagle Squadrons of WW II. Americans in the RAF flew Hurricane MK IIA's with this unit from May to August 1941.

The Museum acquired this Hurricane MK IIA through an exchange with RRS Aviation of Hawkins, Texas, which also restored the aircraft.

CESSNA UC-78B "BOBCAT"

The UC-78 is a military version of the commercial Cessna T-50 light transport. Cessna first produced the wood and tubular steel, fabric-covered T-50 in 1939 for the civilian market. In 1940, the Air Corps ordered them under the designation AT-8 as multi-engine advanced trainers.

Thirty-three AT-8s were built for the Air Corps, and production continued under the designation AT-17, reflecting a change in equipment and engine types. In 1942, the AAF adopted the Bobcat as a light personnel transport, and those delivered after January 1, 1943, were designated UC-78s. By the end of WWII, Cessna had produced more than 4,600 Bobcats for the AAF, 67 of which were transferred to the U.S. Navy as JRC-1s. In addition, 822 Bobcats had been produced for the Royal Canadian Air Force as the Crane I.

Dubbed the "Bamboo Bomber" by the pilots who flew them, it was one of the aircraft featured in the popular television series "Sky King" of the 1940s and 1950s.

The UC-78 on display is one of 1,806 -Bs built for the AAF. It was acquired by the Museum in 1982.

SPECIFICATIONS
Span: 41 ft. 11 in.
Length: 32 ft. 9 in.
Height: 9 ft. 11 in.
Weight: 5,700 lbs. loaded
Armament: None
Engine: Two Jacobs R-755-9s of 245 hp. ea.
Crew: Two (plus three passengers)
Cost: $31,000

PERFORMANCE
Maximum speed: 175 mph.
Cruising speed: 150 mph.
Range: 750 miles
Service ceiling: 15,000 ft.

SPECIFICATIONS

Span: 47 ft. 8 in.
Length: 34 ft. 2 in.
Height: 9 ft. 2 in.
Weight: 9,300 lbs. maximum
Armament: None
Engine: Two Pratt & Whitney R–985s of 450 hp. ea.
Cost: $57,838

PERFORMANCE

Maximum speed: 219 mph.
Cruising speed: 150 mph.
Range: 1,140 miles
Service ceiling: 18,200 ft.

BEECH C–45H "EXPEDITOR"

The C–45 was the WW II military version of the popular Beechcraft Model 18 commercial light transport. Beech built a total of 4,526 of these aircraft for the Army Air Forces between 1939 and 1945 in four versions, the AT–7 "Navigator" navigation trainer, the AT–11 "Kansan" bombing–gunnery trainer, the C–45 "Expeditor" utility transport and the F–2 for aerial photography and mapping. The AT–7 and AT–11 versions were well–known to WW II navigators and bombardiers, for most of these men received their training in these aircraft. Thousands of AAF pilot cadets also were given advanced training in twin–engine Beech airplanes.

During the early 1950s, Beech completely rebuilt 900 C–45s for the Air Force. They received new serial numbers and were designated C–45Gs and C–45Hs, remaining in service until 1963 for administrative and light cargo duties.

The aircraft on display is one of 432 rebuilt as C–45Hs. It was transferred to the U.S. Air Force Museum from the U.S. Federal Reformatory at Chillicothe, Ohio, in 1966.

LOCKHEED C–60A "LODESTAR"

The C-60 is a twin–engine transport based on the Lockheed Model 18 Lodestar. During WW II the Army Air Forces used the aircraft for training and for transporting personnel and freight. First flown in 1940, the Model 18 was originally designed as a successor to the Lockheed Model 14 and the earlier Model 10 Electra. The Army began ordering military versions of the Model 18 in May 1941. Depending upon engines and interior configuration, these transports were given C–56, C–57, C–59 or C–60 basic type designations. Lockheed built more C–60As for the AAF (325) than any other version of the military Lodestar.

After the war, many military Lodestars were declared surplus and sold to private operators for use as cargo or executive transports. The C–60A on display was flown to the USAF Museum in 1981. Eventually it will be restored to its original military configuration.

SPECIFICATIONS

Span: 65 ft. 6 in.
Length: 49 ft. 10 in.
Height: 11 ft. 1 in.
Weight: 18,500 lbs. max.
Armament: None
Engines: Two Wright R–1820–87s of 1,200 hp. ea.
Crew: Four plus 17 passengers
Cost: $123,000

PERFORMANCE

Maximum speed: 257 mph.
Cruising speed: 232 mph.
Range: 1,700 miles
Service ceiling: 25,000 ft.

SPECIFICATIONS

Span: 29 ft. 4 in.
Length: 23 ft. 11 in.
Height: 8 ft. 91/2 in.
Weight: 1,825 lbs. loaded
Armament: None
Engine: DeHavilland Gipsy
Major 1 of 120hp

PERFORMANCE

Maximum speed: 104 mph.
Cruising speed: 90 mph.
Range: 300 miles
Service ceiling: 14,000 ft.

DEHAVILLAND DH-82A "TIGER MOTH"

This classic British trainer made its first flight on October 26, 1931. It is one of a number of models of light aircraft named for moths in recognition of designer Geoffrey DeHavilland's interest in moths and butterflies. It became popular with air forces throughout the British Empire as well as the civilian aviation market. In Britain, 8,101 were manufactured plus 2,751 more in Canada, Australia, and New Zealand. During WWII most Royal Air Force pilots trained in Tiger Moths including Americans who flew with the Eagle Squadrons before the U.S. entered the war. In the United Kingdom, Tiger Moths performed a variety of roles in addition to that of primary trainer including submarine patrol, air ambulance, and even prisoner evacuation. The U.S. Army Air Forces in 1942 ordered 200 from DeHavilland of Canada as the PT-24, but these were never delivered and were diverted to the Royal Canadian Air Force instead.

The beautifully restored Tiger Moth on display at the U.S. Air Force Museum has won numerous trophies at air shows, including a prestigious Category Championship for WWII airplanes at the annual show at Oshkosh, Wisconsin. It was donated to the Museum in August 1998 by Susan and Kurt Hofschneider of Colonia, New Jersey.

VULTEE BT–13B "VALIANT"

The "Valiant" was the basic trainer most widely used by the USAAF during WW II. It represented the second of the three stages of pilot training—primary, basic and advanced. Compared with the primary trainers in use at the time, it was considerably more complex. The BT–13 not only had a more powerful engine, it was also faster and heavier. In addition, it required the student pilot to use two–way radio communications with the ground, operate landing flaps and a two–position variable pitch propeller.

Nicknamed the "Vibrator" by the pilots who flew it, the BT–13 was powered by a Pratt & Whitney R–985 engine. But to counter the shortage of these engines early in the BT–13 production program, 1,693 Valiants were produced in 1941–2 with a Wright R–975 engine and were designated as BT–15s. By the end of WW II, 10,375 BT–13s and BT–15s had been accepted by the AAF.

The BT–13B on display, one of 1,775 Bs built, was acquired from Mr. Raymond Brandly of West Carrollton, Ohio, in 1965.

SPECIFICATIONS

Span: 42 ft. 2 in.
Length: 28 ft. 8 1/2 in.
Height: 12 ft. 4 3/4 in.
Weight: 4,227 lbs. loaded
Armament: None
Engine: Pratt & Whitney R–985 of 450 hp.
Crew: Two (instructor & student)
Cost: $20,000

PERFORMANCE

Maximum speed: 155 mph.
Cruising speed: 130 mph.
Range: 880 miles
Service ceiling: 19,400 ft.

SPECIFICATIONS

Span: 35 ft. 11 3/16 in.
Length: 27 ft. 8 3/8 in.
Height: 7 ft. 9 in.
Weight: 2,450 lbs. loaded
Armament: None
Engine: Ranger L–440
of 175 hp.

PERFORMANCE

Maximum speed: 124 mph.
Cruising speed: 106 mph.
Range: 480 miles
Service ceiling: 16,000 ft.

FAIRCHILD PT–19A "CORNELL"

The PT–19, developed by Fairchild in 1938 to satisfy a military requirement for a rugged monoplane primary trainer, was ordered into quantity production in 1940. In addition to being manufactured by Fairchild during WW II, the "Cornell" was produced in the U.S. by the Aeronca, Howard and St. Louis Aircraft Corporations and in Canada by Fleet Aircraft, Ltd.

Some Cornells were powered by Continental radial engines and designated PT–23s, while others were produced with cockpit canopies and designated PT–26s. Altogether, 7,742 Cornells were manufactured for the AAF, with 4,889 of them being PT–19s. Additional Cornells were supplied to Canada, Norway, Brazil, Ecuador and Chile.

The PT–19A on display was donated to the Air Force Museum in 1984 by Mr. Howard Phillips of Seattle, Washington.

RYAN PT–22 "RECRUIT"

Primary trainers represented the first of three stages of military flight training—primary, basic, and advanced. Prior to 1939, the Air Corps relied entirely on biplanes as primary trainers, but in 1940 it ordered a small number of Ryan low–wing civilian trainers and designated them as PT–16s. They were so successful that the Air Corps then ordered large numbers of improved versions, among them the PT–22. By the time production was completed in 1942, 1,023 PT–22s had been delivered. Twenty–five additional trainers, ordered for the Netherlands, were taken over by the Air Corps in 1942 and designated as PT–22As.

The PT–22 on display was donated by Mrs. Nicholas A. Romano, Jr. and her son, Nicky, of Hampton, Virginia, in 1969 in memory of her husband who lost his life in Vietnam on July 1, 1968, in the crash of an airplane he was piloting. Chief Warrant Officer Romano had served as an enlisted man in the USAF for 22 years prior to retiring. He then enlisted in the U.S. Army to attend flight school and become a pilot. The airplane was restored by the Department of Aviation Technology, Purdue University.

SPECIFICATIONS

Span: 30 ft. 1 in.
Length: 22 ft. 7 1/2 in.
Height: 7 ft. 2 in.
Weight: 1,860 lbs. maximum
Armament: None
Engine: Kinner R–540 of 160 hp.
Cost: $10,000

PERFORMANCE

Maximum speed: 125 mph.
Cruising speed: 100 mph.
Range: 205 miles
Service ceiling: 15,400 ft.

SPECIFICATIONS

Span: 40 ft. 4 in.
Length: 31 ft. 8 in.
Height: 9 ft. 10 in.
Weight: 6,062 lbs. loaded
Armament: None
Engines: Two Lycoming R–680–9s of 295 hp. ea.
Crew: Two
Cost: $34,900

PERFORMANCE

Maximum speed: 197 mph.
Cruising speed: 173 mph.
Range: 750 miles
Service ceiling: 19,000 ft.

CURTISS AT–9 "FLEDGLING"

The AT–9 advanced trainer was used to bridge the gap between single–engine trainers and twin–engine combat aircraft. The prototype first flew in 1941, and the production version entered service in 1942. The prototype had a fabric–covered steel tube fuselage and fabric–covered wings, but production AT–9s were of stressed metal skin construction. The AT–9 was not easy to fly or land, which made it particularly suitable for teaching new pilots to cope with the demanding flight characteristics of a new generation of high–performance, multi–engine aircraft such as the Martin B–26 and Lockheed P–38. Although the AT–9 originally bore the nickname "Fledgling," it was more widely known as the "Jeep." Four hundred ninety–one AT-9s and 300 AT-9As were built before production ended in February 1943.

The aircraft on display was not complete when the USAF Museum acquired it. Some of the parts used to restore it were taken from another incomplete AT–9, while other parts had to be built from "scratch" by Museum restoration specialists.

BEECH AT–11 "KANSAN"

The AT–11 was the standard WW II bombing trainer; about 90 percent of the more than 45,000 AAF bombardiers trained in AT–11s. Like the C–45 transport and AT–7 navigation trainer, the Kansan was a military version of the Beechcraft Model 18 commercial transport. Modifications included a transparent nose, a bomb–bay, internal bomb racks, and provisions for flexible guns for gunnery training.

Student bombardiers normally dropped 100–lb. sand–filled practice bombs. In 1943, the AAF established a minimum proficiency standard of 22 percent hits on target for trainees. Combat training missions were flown taking continuous evasive action within a ten–mile radius of the target and final target approaches had to be straight and level and no longer than 60 seconds. After September 30, 1943, these missions were generally flown using the Norden bombsight and the C–1 automatic pilot, the aircraft being guided by the bombardier student during the bombing run.

The AT–11 on display is one of 1,582 ordered by the AAF between 1941 and 1945, 36 of which were modified as AT–11A navigation trainers. It was donated to the Museum by the Abrams Aerial Survey Corp., Lansing, Michigan, in 1969 and is painted to represent a trainer in service during the autumn of 1943.

SPECIFICATIONS
Span: 47 ft. 7 3/4 in.
Length: 34 ft. 1 7/8 in.
Height: 9 ft. 7 3/4 in.
Weight: 9,300 lbs. maximum
Armament: Two .30–cal. machine guns when used as gunnery trainer
Engines: Two Prattt & Whitney R–985s of 450 hp. ea.
Cost: $67,000

PERFORMANCE
Maximum speed: 215 mph.
Cruising speed: 150 mph.
Range: 745 miles
Service ceiling: 20,000 ft.

Span: 50 ft. 11 in.
Length: 34 ft. 3 in.
Height: 9 ft. 10 in.
Weight: 3,385 lbs.
Armament: None
Engine: Lycoming R–680
of 295 hp.
Cost: $21,000

PERFORMANCE

Maximum speed: 122 mph.
Cruising speed: 109 mph.
Range: 280 miles
Service ceiling: 18,000 ft.

VULTEE L–1A "VIGILANT"

The L–l liaison aircraft, originally designated 0–49, was the military version of the civilian Stinson Model 74. It marked the transition between heavier and larger observation aircraft used by the Air Corps in the 1930s and the lighter liaison "grasshopper" type aircraft represented by the L–series during WW II. Between 1939 and 1941, the Army Air Corps ordered 142 L–1s and 182 L–1As with a 13–inch longer fuselage. Equipped with full–span automatic slats on the leading edge of the wings and pilot–operated slotted flaps on the trailing edge, Vigilants were well–suited for operations from short fields.

Due to its versatility, the Vigilant was used for a variety of missions both in the U.S. and overseas during WW II, including towing training gliders, artillery spotting, liaison duty, emergency rescue, transporting supplies, special espionage missions behind Japanese lines and even for dropping light bombs. Some Vigilants were converted as ambulance aircraft, sometimes fitted with skis or with floats for water takeoffs and landings.

This L–1A, painted as an ambulance conversion, was donated by Mrs. Lawrence Flahart, Anchorage, Alaska, in memory of her husband who began rebuilding it but passed away before finishing it. Restoration was completed for the USAF Museum by the Department of Aviation Technology, Purdue University; it went on display in 1979.

AERONCA L–3B "GRASSHOPPER"

The L–3 liaison aircraft, originally designated 0–58, is the military version of the Aeronca Model 65 "Defender." This high–wing, light airplane could operate from small, hastily–built flying fields. The Army ordered the first 0–58s in 1941 to test the use of light aircraft for liaison and observation missions in direct support of ground forces. Between 1941 and 1943, Aeronca Aircraft Corp. of Middletown, Ohio, built more than 1,400 of these aircraft for the Army—875 of them were L–3Bs. During WW II, Aeronca L–3s joined similar "Grasshoppers" built by Interstate (L–6s), Piper (L–4s) and Taylorcraft (L–2s) for such duties as artillery fire direction, courier service, front–line liaison and pilot training. In 1942, Aeronca developed the TG–5, a training glider based on the 0–58. The three–seat glider had a new front fuselage replacing the engine, but it retained the rear fuselage, wings and tail of the powered version. Aeronca built 250 TG–5s for the Army.

The L–3B on display was built during WW II and found its way into private hands as surplus after the war. Completely restored by its previous owner, Paul Grice of Waynesville, Ohio, the airplane was flown to the Museum on May 29, 1984.

SPECIFICATIONS

Span: 35 ft.
Length: 21 ft.
Height: 7 ft. 8 in.
Weight: 1,300 lbs. max.
Armament: None
Engine: One Continental 0–170–3 of 65 hp.
Crew: Two
Cost: $2,826

PERFORMANCE

Maximum speed: 87 mph.
Cruising speed: 79 mph.
Range: 199 miles
Service ceiling: 7,750 ft.

SPECIFICATIONS

Span: 35 ft. 3 in.
Length: 22 ft. 5 in.
Height: 6 ft. 8 in.
Weight: 1,200 lbs. maximum
Armament: None
Engine: Continental O–170 of 65 hp
Cost: $2,600

PERFORMANCE

Maximum speed: 85 mph
Cruising speed: 75 mph
Range: 190 miles
Service ceiling: 9,300 ft.

PIPER L–4 "GRASSHOPPER"

The L–4 liaison aircraft, originally designated the O–59, was the military version of the famous Piper J3 "Cub." The Army ordered the first O–59s in 1941 for tests in conjunction with its growing interest in the use of light aircraft for liaison and observation duties in direct support of ground forces. Between 1941 and 1945, the Army procured more than 5,000 L–4s from Piper.

During WW II, "Grasshoppers" performed a wide variety of functions throughout the world such as for artillery fire direction, pilot training, glider pilot instruction, courier service and front–line liaison.

The L-4 on display is painted and marked to represent one of the aircraft that flew in support of the Allied invasion of North Africa in November 1942. It was placed on display in April 1995.

STINSON L–5 "SENTINEL"

The L–5 was the military version of the commercial Stinson 105 Voyager. Six Voyagers were purchased by the AAF in 1941 as YO–54s for testing, and quantity orders for Sentinels began in 1942, first as O–62s before the designation was changed to "L" for liaison in April 1942. Between 1942–5, the AAF ordered 3,590 L–5s, making it the second most widely used AAF liaison aircraft. The unarmed L–5 with its short field takeoff and landing capability was used for reconnaissance, removing litter patients from front line areas, delivering supplies to isolated units, laying communications wire, spotting enemy targets for attack aircraft, transporting personnel, rescuing Allied personnel in remote areas, and even as a light bomber. In Asia and the Pacific, L–5s sometimes took off and landed literally over the heads of enemy troops. Some L–5s remained in service with USAF units as late as 1955.

The L–5 on display was donated by Dr. Robert R. Kundel of Rice Lake, Wisconsin and was restored by the "Oriole Club" 133d Tactical Airlift Wing, Minnesota ANG. It is marked and painted as an L–5 of the 25th Liaison Squadron serving in New Guinea in 1944. It was delivered to the Museum in 1977.

SPECIFICATIONS

Span: 34 ft. 0 in.
Length: 24 ft. 1 in.
Height: 8 ft. 11 1/2 in.
Weight: 2,050 lbs. max.
Armament: None
Engine: Lycoming 0–435–1 of 190 hp.
Cost: $10,000

PERFORMANCE

Maximum speed: 130 mph.
Cruising speed: 90 mph.
Range: 360 miles
Service ceiling: 15,600 ft.

SPECIFICATIONS

Span: 34 ft. 0 in.
Length: 30 ft. 2 in.
Height: 12 ft. 5 in.
Weight: 7,570 lbs. normal load
Armament: One 37mm cannon firing through prop hub; two .50–cal. machine guns in nose; two .50–cal. machine guns in packets under wing; 500 lbs. of bombs externally.
Engine: Allison V–1710 of 1,200 hp.
Cost: $46,000

PERFORMANCE

Maximum speed: 376 mph.
Cruising speed: 250 mph.
Range: 650 miles
Service ceiling: 35,000 ft.

BELL P–39Q "AIRACOBRA"

The P–39 was one of America's first–line pursuit planes in December 1941. It made its initial flight in April 1939 at Wright Field and by the time of the Pearl Harbor attack, nearly 600 had been built. Its unique engine location behind the cockpit caused some pilot concern, but this proved not to be any more of a hazard in a crash landing than with an engine located forward of the cockpit. However, the P–39's spin characteristics could be quite a problem if proper recovery techniques were ignored.

The Airacobra saw combat throughout the world, particularly in the Southwest Pacific, Mediterranean and Russian theaters. Because its engine was not equipped with a supercharger, the P–39 performed best below 17,000 feet altitude, and it often was used at lower altitudes for such missions as ground strafing. When P–39 production ended in August 1944, Bell had built 9,584 Airacobras, of which 4,773 had been allotted to the Soviet Union. Russian pilots particularly liked the cannon–armed P–39 for its ground–attack capability. Other P–39s served with French and British forces.

The P–39Q on display was obtained by the Air Force Museum Foundation from the Hardwick Aircraft Co., El Monte, California in 1966. It is painted as a P–39J flown by Lt. Leslie Spoonts of the 57th Fighter Squadron in 1942 while based on Kodiak and Adak Islands during the Aleutian Campaign.

NORTH AMERICAN A–36A "APACHE"

The A–36A dive bomber was the first AAF version of the "Mustang" developed for Britain in 1940. The A–36 first flew in October 1942; production of 500 A–36As was completed by March 1943.

Unofficially named "Invaders," A–36As were assigned to the 27th and 86th Bombardment Groups (Dive), later redesignated as Fighter–Bomber Groups. In June 1943, the plane went into action from North Africa. During the Italian campaign, A–36A pilots flew bomber escort and strafing missions as well as ground support bombing attacks. A–36As also served with the 311th Fighter Bomber Group in India. Dive brakes in the wings gave greater stability in a dive, but they were sometimes wired closed due to malfunctions. In 1944, AAF A–36As were replaced by P–51s and P–47s when experience showed that these high–altitude fighters, equipped with bomb racks, were more suitable for low–level missions than A–36As.

The aircraft on display was obtained in 1971. It was restored by the 148th Fighter–Interceptor Group, Minnesota ANG. It is painted as the A–36A flown by Capt. Lawrence Dye, 522nd Fighter–Bomber Sq, in Tunisia, Sicily and Italy during WW II.

SPECIFICATIONS
Span: 37 ft.
Length: 32 ft. 3 in.
Height: 12 ft. 2 in.
Weight: 10,000 lbs. loaded
Armament: Six .50–cal. machine guns; 1,000 lbs. of bombs externally
Engine: Allison V–1710 of 1,325 hp.
Cost: $49,000

PERFORMANCE
Maximum speed: 365 mph.
Cruising speed: 250 mph.
Range: 550 miles
Service ceiling: 25,100 ft.

SPECIFICATIONS

Span: 104 ft.
Length: 63 ft. 10 in.
Height: 20 ft. 1 in.
Weight: 36,400 lbs. loaded
Armament: Two .50–cal. machine guns in the waist and two .30–cal. machine guns— one in the bow and another in a rear tunnel—plus 8,000 lbs. of bombs
Engines: Two Pratt & Whitney R–1830–92s of 1,200 hp. ea.
Crew: Eight
Cost: $50,000

PERFORMANCE

Maximum Speed: 184 mph.
Cruising speed: 120 mph.
Range: 2,325 miles
Service ceiling: 22,400 ft.

CONSOLIDATED OA-10 "CATALINA"

The OA–10 is the Army Air Force's version of the PBY series seaplanes and amphibians flown extensively by the Navy during WW II. It is a twin–engine, parasol–wing monoplane equipped with a flying boat hull, retractable tricycle landing gear and retractable wing tip floats. The OA–10 was used primarily for air–sea rescue work ("DUMBO" missions) with the AAF's Emergency Rescue Squadrons throughout WW II and for several years thereafter. During the war, OA–10 crews rescued hundreds of downed fliers.

The prototype Catalina first flew on March 28, 1935. It was produced by Consolidated Aircraft Corp. in both seaplane and amphibian versions. Catalinas were also produced by Canadian Vickers, Ltd. and the Naval Aircraft Factory. Eventually, nearly 2,500 Catalina derivatives were built for the Navy. Approximately 380 were transferred to the AAF as OA–10s, OA–10As, OA–10Bs or, in some cases, with their original Navy designations. Catalinas also were flown by a number of allied nations during and after WW II.

This aircraft was operated extensively by the Brazilian Air Force until 1981 in a variety of humanitarian roles in the Amazon Basin. The Catalina was flown to the Museum in 1984 and has been restored and painted as an OA–10A assigned to the 2nd Emergency Rescue Squadron which served in the Pacific Theater during WW II.

DOUGLAS B–23 "DRAGON"

The B–23 was a twin–engine bomber developed as a successor to the Douglas B–18. First flown in July 1939, the B–23 incorporated many features of the Douglas DC–3 commercial transport. Although it was much faster than the B–18 and was the first operational Army bomber equipped with a tail gun, the Dragon was soon outclassed by more modern bombers such as the North American B–25 and the Martin B–26. As a result, only 38 B–23s were built.

The B–23s were never used in combat during WW II. Instead, they served in secondary roles as reconnaissance, training, transport, and test–bed aircraft. Some of the Dragons used in transport service were redesignated UC–67s.

After the war, all B–23s/UC–67s were declared surplus and many were sold to private operators for use as cargo and executive transports. Several of these aircraft were still flying in the early 1980s. The Museum's B–23, acquired in 1982, will require extensive restoration.

SPECIFICATIONS
Span: 92 ft.
Length: 58 ft. 6 in.
Height: 18 ft. 6 in.
Weight: 32,400 lbs. max.
Armament: Three .30–cal. M–2 machine guns, one .50–cal. M–2 machine gun, plus 4,000 lbs. of bombs carried internally
Engines: Two Wright R–2600–3s of 1,600 hp. ea.
Crew: Six
Cost: $133,000

PERFORMANCE
Maximum speed: 282 mph.
Cruising speed: 210 mph.
Range: 1,400 miles
Service ceiling: 31,600 ft.

SPECIFICATIONS

Span: 34 ft. 8 in.
Length: 27 ft. 6 in.
Height: 10 ft.
Weight: 5,275 lbs. loaded
Armament: Two 12.7mm Breda machine guns firing through the propeller.
Engines: One FIAT A.74 R.C.38 double row, fourteen cylinder, air cooled radial engine of 870 hp.
Crew: One

PERFORMANCE

Maximum speed: 313 mph/ 272 knots.
Range: 355 miles/ 308 nautical miles
Endurance: 1 hr. 20 min.
Ceiling: 29,200 ft.

MACCHI MC-200 "SAETTA" (LIGHTNING)

Developed in the mid-1930s for the Italian Royal Air Force (Regia Aeronautica), the "Saetta" was one of the principal fighters with which Italy entered the Second World War. The prototype made its first flight in December 1937, and by Italy's entry into World War II in June 1940 some 156 were in service. The MC-200 was first employed against the British at Malta and eventually saw service in Greece, North Africa, Yugoslavia, and the Soviet Union. Saettas were employed against U.S. forces in North Africa and over Italy itself. A total of 1,151 were produced.

The MC-200 on display was transferred from the Regia Aeronautica's 372nd Squadron in Italy to the 165th Squadron in North Africa during November 1942 just in time to be abandoned at the Benghazi K3 airfield during the Axis retreat following the battle of El Alamein. Apparently in the press of circumstances it remained in its 372nd Squadron markings. It was first taken by British forces, but was subsequently shipped to the United States where it was exhibited around the country to sell war bonds. It was eventually obtained by the New England Air Museum. Then, in 1989 it was purchased by a private owner who had it restored in Italy by a team from Aermacchi, the original builder, before its acquisition by the USAF Museum. It is displayed in the markings of the 372nd Squadron of the Regia Aeronautica which it carried at the time of its capture.

JUNKERS Ju 52/3M

The Ju 52 tri-motor, like the USAF C–47, was first built in the 1930s yet remained in service for more than a quarter century. This transport made its maiden flight in April 1931 and three years later a heavy bomber version appeared. The latter aircraft formed the nucleus of the Luftwaffe's infant bomber force in the mid–1930s and it was used during the Spanish Civil War.

The Ju 52 was obsolete as a bomber by 1939, but because of its durability, simplicity of design, and handling characteristics it continued to serve throughout WW II as a versatile workhorse of the German transport fleet. For a period, Adolph Hitler used a Ju 52 as his private transport. Ju 52s delivered the attacking forces and their supplies during the German invasion of Norway, Denmark, France, and the Low Countries in 1940. Almost 500 Ju 52s participated in the historic airborne assault on the island of Crete in May 1941 and Junkers later supplied Rommel's armored forces in North Africa.

Approximately 30 different countries have flown Ju 52s. The aircraft on display was donated to the Museum by the Spanish Government in 1971.

SPECIFICATIONS
(transport version)
Span: 95 ft. 11 1/2 in.
Length: 62 ft. 0 in.
Height: 18 ft. 2 1/2 in.
Weight: 24,250 lbs. max.
Armament: Four 7.9mm machine guns
Engines: Three BMW 132T–2 engines of 830 hp. ea.

PERFORMANCE
(transport version)
Maximum speed: 178 mph.
Cruising speed: 134 mph.
Range: 810 miles
Service ceiling: 19,360 ft.

SPECIFICATIONS

Span: 46 ft. 9 in.
Length: 32 ft. 6 in.
Height: 10 ft. 0 in.
Weight: 2,904 lbs. max.
Armament: None (some Storches carried one 7.9mm MG–15 machine gun)
Engine: One Argus As 10C–3 of 240 hp.

PERFORMANCE

Maximum speed: 109 mph.
Cruising speed: 93 mph.
Range: 238 miles
Service ceiling: 17,300 ft.

FIESELER Fi 156C "STORCH"

The Storch (Stork) was designed in 1935 and was widely used during WW II by German military forces for reconnaissance, liaison, ambulance, and other duties and by high ranking officers as personal transports. Among its features was its maneuverability, extremely low stalling speed of 32 mph (51 km/hr), and its short field takeoff and landing characteristics. Between 1937–45, the German Air Force accepted almost 2,900 Storches. Other countries using the Fi 156 included Sweden, Finland, Switzerland, and Italy. The most famous Storch mission was the hazardous rescue of deposed Italian dictator Benito Mussolini in 1943 from a tiny rock–strewn plateau at a remote lodge high in the Appennine Mountains.

This aircraft is painted as the Storch used by Field Marshal Erwin Rommel in North Africa. Built in 1940, it was exported to Sweden where it remained until 1948. The last German to fly it before its acquisition by the donors in 1973 was German WW II ace Erich Hartmann. The pilot on its final flight was Brig. Gen. "Chuck" Yeager, USAF, first man to exceed Mach 1 in the Bell X–l. It was donated by Lt. Col. Perry A. Schreffler, USAFR, and Maj. Robert C. Van Ausdell, USAFR, of Santa Paula, California, and was delivered to the Museum in 1974.

JUNKERS Ju 88D

The German Ju 88 was one of the most versatile airplanes of WW II. It was used in practically every kind of combat role, including dive bomber, level bomber, night fighter, day interceptor, photo reconnaissance, tank destroyer, and even as a "pilotless missile." Although the Ju 88 made its first flight on December 21, 1936, hundreds were still in use when the war ended in 1945.

The airplane on display is a Ju 88D, a long–range photo reconnaissance version. It is the famous "Baksheesh," the best known Ju 88 of all the 15,000 built. On July 22, 1943, it was flown to Cyprus by a defecting Rumanian Air Force pilot who had become disillusioned with his German Luftwaffe superior officers. It was then flown by U.S. pilots across the South Atlantic Ocean to Wright Field where it was tested extensively. In 1946 the airplane was placed in storage in Arizona; it was shipped to the U.S. Air Force Museum in January 1960.

SPECIFICATIONS
Span: 65 ft. 10 in.
Length: 47 ft. 1 in.
Height: 15 ft. 11 in.
Weight: 26,700 lbs.
Armament: Six 7.9 mm machine guns
Engines: Two Junkers Jumo 211s of 1,200 hp. ea.

PERFORMANCE
Maximum speed: 295 mph.
Cruising speed: 225 mph.
Range: 1,553 miles
Service ceiling: 27,880 ft.

SPECIFICATIONS

Span: 34 ft. 5 1/3 in.
Length: 33 ft. 5 1/4 in.
Height: 11 ft. 0 1/4 in.
Weight: 10,670 lbs.
combat–loaded
Armament: Two 20mm MG 151 cannons in wings and two 13mm MG 131 machine guns in nose
Engine: Junkers Jumo 213 of 2,240 hp. with methanol–water injection

PERFORMANCE

Maximum speed: 426 mph.
Cruising speed: 280 mph.
Range: 520 miles
Service ceiling: 40,000 ft.

FOCKE–WULF Fw 190D

The Fw 190, one of Germany's best fighter airplanes of WW II, made its first flight on June 1, 1939. It appeared in action over northwestern France in September 1941 and rapidly proved its superiority over the Mark V Spitfire, Britain's best fighter at the time.

Most Fw 190s were of the "A" series, powered by a BMW radial engine. Late in 1943, however, the "D" series appeared in action against U.S. bombers, powered by the Jumo 213 in-line, liquid–cooled engine. With its more powerful engine, the "D" had better performance than the "A" but because of its lengthened nose, a 20–inch section had to be added to the fuselage just forward of the tail. During its lifetime, more than 20,000 Fw 190s of all types were built.

The Fw 190D on display was assigned to the JG3 "Udet" Geschwader, one of the Luftwaffe's most famous fighter units which was named for Ernest Udet, Germany's leading ace to survive WW I. The airplane was captured and brought to the U.S. for testing at the end of WW II. It is on loan from the National Air and Space Museum of the Smithsonian Institution.

MESSERSCHMITT Me 163B "KOMET"

The German Me 163, a rocket powered defensive fighter, was one of the most interesting aircraft of World War II. Fortunately, its potential impact was minimized by technical problems and the small number produced.

The first Me 163 prototypes were tested in 1941, but powered flight testing of the more advanced Me 163B was delayed until August 1943 by engine and fuel problems. Although the Komet's rocket engine gave it an exceptional climb rate, range was severely limited by its high fuel consumption. Furthermore, the fuels used were extremely hazardous and sometimes exploded without warning.

Production Me 163Bs were not ready for operational use until July 1944. The Luftwaffe planned to have small units of Komets dispersed to intercept Allied bomber formations, but only 279 Me 163Bs were delivered by the end of the war. The sole operational Komet group, JG 400 scored nine kills while losing 14 of its own aircraft.

Indications were found that the Me 163B on display may have been sabotaged while under construction, perhaps by the forced laborers building it in Germany.

SPECIFICATIONS
Span: 30 ft. 7 1/3 in.
Length: 19 ft. 2 1/3 in.
Height: (on take-off dolly) 9 ft 2/3in.
Armament: Two 30mm MK 108 cannon
Engine: Walter HWK 509A-2 rocket with 3,748 lb thrust

PERFORMANCE
Maximum speed: 596 mph.
Initial climb rate: 16,000 ft/min
Range: about 50 miles
Service ceiling: 39,500 ft.
Maximum powered endurance: 7 1/2 min.

SPECIFICATIONS

Span: 41 ft.
Length: 34 ft. 9 in.
Height: 11 ft. 4 in.
Weight: 15,600 lbs.
Armament: Four 30mm MK–108 cannons, plus 1,000 lbs. of bombs.
Engines: Two Junkers Jumo 004s of 1,980 lbs. thrust each.
Crew: One

PERFORMANCE

Maximum speed: 540 mph.
Cruising speed: 460 mph.
Range: 650 miles.
Service Ceiling: 38,000 ft.

MESSERSCHMITT Me 262A "SCHWALBE"

Developed from a 1938 design by the Messerschmitt company, the Me 262 "Schwalbe," ("Swallow") was the world's first operational turbojet aircraft. First flown as a pure jet on July 18, 1942, it proved much faster than conventional airplanes. Development problems, Allied bombings, and cautious Luftwaffe leadership contributed to delays in quantity production. In late 1943, Adolf Hitler agreed to mass production, but insisted the aircraft be used primarily as a fighter–bomber. On July 25, 1944, an Me 262 became the first jet airplane used in combat when it attacked a British photo–reconnaissance Mosquito flying over Munich. As a fighter, the German jet scored heavily against Allied bomber formations. The bombers, however, destroyed hundreds of Me 262s on the ground. More than 1,400 Me 262s were produced, but fewer than 300 saw combat. Most remained on the ground awaiting conversion to bombers, or were unable to fly because of lack of fuel, spare parts, or trained pilots.

The Me 262A on display was brought to the U.S. from Germany in July 1945 for flight evaluation. It was restored by the 96th Mobile Maintenance Squadron, Kelly AFB, Texas in 1976–79, and is finished in the standard production paint scheme, without operational unit markings.

DᴇHAVILLAND DH–98 "MOSQUITO"

The famous British Mosquito—known to many as "Mossie"—was a versatile aircraft used extensively during World War II. Constructed primarily of plywood with a balsa wood core, it had excellent speed, altitude and range. First flown on November 25, 1940, the Mosquito entered production in mid–1941 and was produced until well after the end of the war. Almost 8,000 Mossies were built in Great Britain, Canada and Australia. Although best known for their service with the Royal Air Force, Mosquitoes were also used by several U.S. Army Air Forces units for photo and weather reconnaissance, and as night fighters. During the war, the AAF acquired 40 Canadian Mossies and flew them under the American F–8 (photo reconnaissance) designation. In addition, the British turned over more than 100 Mosquitoes to the AAF under Reverse Lend-Lease. These aircraft retained their British designations.

The aircraft on display is a British–built B. Mk. 35 manufactured in 1946 (later converted for towing targets) and is similar to the P.R. Mk. XVIs used by the AAF. It was flown to the Museum in February 1985. This Mosquito has been restored to a Mk. XVI configuration and painted as a weather reconnaissance aircraft of the 653rd Bomb Squadron, 25th Bomb Group, based in England in 1944–45.

SPECIFICATIONS

Span: 54 ft. 2 in.
Length: 40 ft. 6 in.
Height: 12 ft. 6 in.
Weight: 23,000 lbs. loaded
Armament: 4,000 lbs. of bombs in bomber version
Engines: Two Rolls–Royce Merlins of 1,690 hp. ea.
Crew: Two
Cost: $100,000 approx.

PERFORMANCE

Maximum speed: 415 mph.
Cruising speed: 276 mph.
Range: 1,955 miles
Service ceiling: 42,000 ft.

SPECIFICATIONS
Rotor diameter: 38 ft.
Length: 33 ft. 7 3/4 in.
Height: 12 ft. 5 in.
Weight: 2,581 lbs. loaded
Armament: None
Engine: Warner R–550
of 200 hp.

SPECIFICATIONS

Rotor diameter: 38 ft.
Length: 33 ft. 7 3/4 in.
Height: 12 ft. 5 in.
Weight: 2,581 lbs. loaded
Armament: None
Engine: Warner R–550
of 200 hp.

PERFORMANCE

Maximum speed: 75 mph.
Cruising speed: 65 mph.
Range: 130 miles
Service ceiling: 8,000 ft.

SIKORSKY R–4B "HOVERFLY"

The R–4 was the world's first production helicopter and the Air Force's first service helicopter. The original military model, the XR–4, was developed from the famous experimental VS–300 helicopter, invented by Igor Sikorsky and publicly demonstrated in 1940. The XR–4 made its initial flight on January 13, 1942 and as a result of its successful flight tests, the AAF ordered 3 YR–4As and 27 YR–4Bs for service testing and flight training. Of these 30, one went to Burma and one to Alaska, while several others were assigned to the U.S. Navy, U.S. Coast Guard and British Royal Navy. They showed such promise that the AAF ordered 100 R–4Bs.

The R–4 was first used in combat in May 1944. In a letter to a friend, Col. Philip G. Cochran, CO of the 1st Air Commando Group, wrote: "Today the 'egg–beater' went into action and the damn thing acted like it had good sense."

The R–4B on display was donated by the University of Illinois in 1967.

WACO CG–4A

The CG–4A was the most widely used U.S. troop/cargo glider of WW II. Flight testing began in 1942 and eventually more than 12,000 CG–4As were procured. Fifteen companies manufactured CG–4As, with 1,074 built by the Waco Aircraft Company of Troy, Ohio.

The CG–4A was constructed of fabric–covered wood and metal and was crewed by a pilot and copilot. It could carry 13 troops and their equipment or either a jeep, a quarter–ton truck, or a 75mm howitzer loaded through the upward–hinged nose section. C–46s and C–47s were usually used as tow aircraft.

CG–4As went into operation in July 1943 during the Allied invasion of Sicily. They participated in the D–Day assault on France on June 6, 1944, and in other important airborne operations in Europe and in the China–Burma–India Theater. Until late in the war, gliders were generally considered expendable in combat and were abandoned or destroyed after landing.

The glider on display, built by the Gibson Refrigerator Company in Greenville, Michigan, is marked as it appeared when it was accepted by the U.S. Army Air Forces in July, 1945.

SPECIFICATIONS

Span: 83 ft. 8 in.
Length: 48 ft. 4 in.
Height: 12 ft. 7 in.
Weight: 7,500 lbs. loaded
Armament: None
Engine: None
Cost: $24,000

PERFORMANCE

Maximum towed speed: 150 mph.

SPECIFICATIONS

Span: 61 ft. 4 in.
Length: 48 ft.
Height: 17 ft. 7 in.
Weight: 26,580 lbs. loaded
Armament: Eight .50–cal. machine guns; 2,000 lbs. of bombs internally; 2,000 lbs. externally
Engines: Two Wright R–2600s of 1,600 hp. ea.
Cost: $74,000

PERFORMANCE

Maximum speed: 317 mph.
Cruising speed: 230 mph.
Range: 1,025 miles
Service ceiling: 25,000 ft.

DOUGLAS A–20G "HAVOC"

When the U.S. entered WW II, the A–20 attack bomber had already been proven in combat by British and French forces. On July 4, 1942, six A–20s flown by American crews of the 15th Bombardment Squadron accompanied six flown by British crews on a low–altitude mission against four Dutch airfields, the first U.S. daylight bombing raid in Europe.

The versatile A–20 was used in the Pacific, Middle East, North African, Russian, and European theaters. Some A–20s, equipped with radar equipment and additional nose guns, were redesignated as P–70s and were used as night fighters until replaced in 1944 by the P–61 "Black Widow" with its increased high altitude performance.

A–20 production halted in September 1944 with more than 7,000 built for the U.S. and its allies. The A–20G was the first series to have a "solid" nose; the aircraft on display is one of 2,850 –Gs built. It is painted in the markings of the 89th Bomb Squadron (Light) which flew the A-20 in combat in the Southwest Pacific for three years during WWII. It was donated by the Bankers Life and Casualty Company of Chicago in 1961.

NOORDUYN UC–64A "NORSEMAN"

The UC–64A is a ten–place, single–engine utility transport manufactured by Noorduyn Aviation, Ltd., Montreal, Canada. First flown in 1935, the Norseman was designed for rugged Canadian bush country operations and could be equipped with wheels, floats, or skis. Before WW II, 69 were delivered to the Royal Canadian Air Force as trainers. After service testing seven YC–64s, the U.S. Army Air Forces adopted the aircraft in 1942 as a light transport. Noorduyn produced 762 Norsemen for the USAAF before the war ended. Of these, 749 were UC–64As, including three that went to the Navy as JA–1s and six that were equipped with floats for the U.S. Army Corps of Engineers. The last Norseman was produced in late 1959.

Designed for and used in arctic areas, the Norseman also was employed in Europe and the Pacific as well as in the U.S. during the war. On December 15, 1944, a UC–64A disappeared on a flight from England to France with bandleader Major Glenn Miller on board. The aircraft was never found.

The Norseman on display was acquired by the Museum in March 1981. It is marked as a Norseman based in Alaska late in WW II.

SPECIFICATIONS
Span: 51 ft. 6 in.
Length: 31 ft. 9 in.
Height: 10 ft. 1 in.
Weight: 7,400 lbs. max.
Armament: None
Engine: One Pratt & Whitney R–1340–AN1 of 600 hp.
Crew: One or two—depending on mission
Cost: $28,000

PERFORMANCE
Maximum speed: 162 mph.
Cruising speed: 148 mph.
Range: 1,150 miles
Service ceiling: 17,000 ft.

SPECIFICATIONS

Span: 66 ft.
Length: 49 ft. 7 in.
Height: 14 ft. 8 in.
Weight: 35,855 lbs. loaded
Armament: Four .50–cal.
machine guns in upper
turret and four 20mm
cannons in belly;
6,400 lbs. of bombs
Engines: Two Pratt & Whitney
R–2800s of 2,100 hp. ea.
Cost: $170,000

PERFORMANCE

Maximum speed: 425 mph.
Cruising speed: 275 mph.
Range: 1,200 miles
Service ceiling: 46,200 ft.

NORTHROP P–61C "BLACK WIDOW"

The heavily–armed Black Widow was this country's first aircraft specifically designed as a night fighter. In the nose, it carried radar equipment which enabled its crew of two or three to locate enemy aircraft in total darkness and fly into proper position to attack.

The XP–61 was flight–tested in 1942 and delivery of production aircraft began in late 1943. The P–61 flew its first operational intercept mission as a night fighter in Europe on July 3, 1944, and later was also used as a night intruder over enemy territory. In the Pacific, a Black Widow claimed its first "kill" on the night of July 6, 1944. As P–61s became available, they replaced interim Douglas P–70s in all USAAF night fighter squadrons. During WW II, Northrop built approximately 700 P–61s; 41 of these were –Cs manufactured in the summer of 1945 offering greater speed and capable of operating at higher altitude. Northrop fabricated 36 more Black Widows in 1946 as F–15A unarmed photo–reconnaissance aircraft.

The Black Widow on display was presented to the U.S. Air Force Museum by the Tecumseh Council, Boy Scouts of America, Springfield, Ohio, in 1958. It is painted and marked as a P–61B assigned to the 550th Night Fighter Squadron serving in the Pacific in 1945.

GRUMMAN OA–12 "DUCK"

The OA–12 "Duck" is the U.S. Air Force version of the Navy J2F–6 amphibian. It was derived from the XJF–1, a Grumman amphibian that flew for the first time in May 1933. Later, Grumman built a variety of JF– and J2F–series aircraft that were used primarily by the Navy, Marine Corps, and Coast Guard, before and during World War II. After the war, air–sea rescue duties assigned to the USAF's Air Rescue Service required special aircraft for overwater missions. So in 1948, the USAF acquired eight surplus Navy J2F–6s for air–sea rescue work. Five were designated OA–12s and sent to Alaska for duty with the 10th Air Rescue Squadron (the other three disappeared from the records and apparently went to an allied country under the Mutual Defense Assistance Program).

The Grumman–designed J2F–6 Duck on display was built by the Columbia Aircraft Corp., of Valley Stream, New York, as were all J2F–6s. It was delivered to the U.S. Coast Guard on 9 June 1945, but was declared surplus in 1946 and sold to a private individual. Since then, it has had a series of civilian owners and a movie career. It "starred" in the film "Murphy's War" in the early 1970s, as well as several others. This aircraft is painted as one of the rescue OA–12s the USAF acquired in 1948.

SPECIFICATIONS

Span: 39 ft.
Length: 34 ft.
Height: 14 ft.
Weight: 7,200 lbs.
Armament: None (provisions for underwing racks for bombs or depth charges)
Engine: One Wright R–1820–54 of 1,050 hp.
Crew: Two
Cost: $69,000

PERFORMANCE

Maximum speed: 188 mph.
Cruising speed: 150 mph.
Range: 780 miles
Service ceiling: 20,000 ft.

SPECIFICATIONS

Span: 45 ft. 6 in.
Length: 38 ft. 10 in.
Height: 11 ft. 11 3/4 in.
Weight: 10,532 lbs. loaded
Armament: One 37mm cannon and three .50–cal. machine guns
Engines: Two General Electric I-16s of 1,650 lbs. thrust each

PERFORMANCE

Maximum speed: 450 mph.
Cruising speed: 320 mph.
Range: 440 miles
Service ceiling: 43,400 ft.

BELL P–59B "AIRACOMET"

Development of the P–59, America's first jet–propelled airplane, was ordered personally by General H. H. Arnold on September 4, 1941. The project was conducted under the utmost secrecy, with Bell building the airplane and General Electric the engine. The first P–59 was completed in mid–1942 and on October 1, 1942, it made its initial flight at Muroc Dry Lake (now Edwards Air Force Base), California. One year later, the airplane was ordered into production, to be powered by I–14 and I–16 engines, improved versions of the original I–A.

Bell produced 66 P–59s. Although the airplane's performance was not spectacular and it never got into combat, the P–59 provided training for AAF personnel and invaluable data for subsequent development of higher performance jet airplanes.

The P–59B on display was obtained from Kirtland Air Force Base, New Mexico in February 1956.

YOKOSUKA MXY7-K1 TRAINER

Late in World War II, the Dai-Ichi Kaigun Koku Gijitsusho (1st Naval Air Technical Arsenal) at Yokosuka, Japan, designed the MXY7-K1 to teach less experienced pilots to fly the Model 11 "Ohka" (Cherry Blossom) kamikaze suicide rocket bomb. The Ohka was carried to the target under a Mitsubishi G4M "Betty" bomber. When the Betty/Ohka combination reached Allied shipping, the Ohka pilot would separate from the bomber, ignite the rocket motor, and dive into a ship.

This trainer version was carried aloft and then released for practice flights. Unlike the Ohka, the MXY7-K1 had a landing skid and flaps. In place of the warhead and rocket motors of the Ohka, the MXY7-K1 used water ballast that was expelled before landing. Even so, it challenged novice pilots with its high, 130 mph landing speed.

A total of 45 MXY7-K1 trainers were completed by the end of World War II.

SPECIFICATIONS
(for operational version, Model 11 "Ohka")

Span: 16 ft. 5 in.
Length: 19 ft. 10 in.
Height: 3 ft. 10 in.
Weight(with warhead): 4,530 lbs.
Armament: 2,646 lb. warhead
Engines: Three Type 4 Mk. 1 rockets with a total of 1,764 lbs.of thrust
Crew: One

PERFORMANCE

Maximum speed: 615 mph.in power dive
Range: 55 miles (unpowered glide, 8-10 seconds of rocket thrust for final dive

SPECIFICATIONS

Span: 70 ft.
Length: 51 ft. 3 in.
Height: 18 ft. 3 in.
Weight: 35,000 lbs. loaded
Armament: Highly variable. A–26C had two forward–firing .50–cal. machine guns and two turrets with two .50–cal. machine guns each. It also carried bombs internally and under wings.
Engines: Two Pratt & Whitney R–2800s of 2,000 hp. ea.
Crew: 3
Cost: $172,000

PERFORMANCE

Maximum speed: 373 mph.
Cruising speed: 284 mph.
Range: 1,400 miles
Service ceiling: 28,000 ft.

DOUGLAS A–26C "INVADER"

The A–26 is a WW II attack bomber used for bombing, ground strafing and rocket attacks. It made its first flight on July 10, 1942. Production deliveries began in August 1943, and on September 6, 1944, the A–26 went into combat over Europe. Approximately 2,500 Invaders had been built when production ended after WW II. Redesignated B–26 in 1948 (thus creating everlasting confusion with the Martin B–26 "Marauder"), the Invader served again during the Korean War (1950–53), mainly as a night intruder against North Korean supply lines. It was removed from service in 1958, but in 1961 the USAF recalled some A–26s for use as tactical bombers in Southeast Asia (SEA). By 1964, combat duty and 20 years of wear had taken their toll and the Invaders were again removed from service. The USAF, however, ordered 40 Invaders to be rebuilt and highly modified with more powerful engines and increased structural strength. Initially designated B–26Ks, they were renamed "Counter Invader," sent to SEA in 1966, and redesignated A–26As.

The A–26C on display was flown to the museum in September 1957. It appears in the colors and markings used during the Korean War by the 34th Bomb Squadron flying night intruder missions.

NORTH AMERICAN F–82B
"TWIN MUSTANG"

The F–82 was the last propeller–driven fighter acquired in quantity by the USAF. It appears to be two Mustang fuselages on one wing, but in reality it was a totally new design. Its purpose was to provide a fighter carrying a pilot and co–pilot/navigator to reduce fatigue on long–range bomber escort missions. Delivery from production did not begin until early 1946, too late for WW II. After WW II, radar–equipped F–82s were used quite extensively by the Air Defense Command as replacements for the P–61 night fighter.

During the Korean Conflict, Japan–based F–82s were among the first USAF aircraft to operate over Korea. The first three North Korean airplanes destroyed by U.S. forces were shot down by all–weather F–82G interceptors on June 27, 1950.

Of a total of 273 F–82s produced, 20 were –Bs. The F–82B on display, "Betty-Jo," flew from Hawaii to New York on February 27–28, 1947, a distance of 5,051 miles, the longest non–stop flight ever made by a prop–driven fighter. "Betty Jo" was delivered to the U.S. Air Force Museum in 1957.

SPECIFICATIONS

Span: 51 ft. 3 in.
Length: 38 ft. 1 in.
Height: 13 ft. 8 in.
Weight: 24,800 lbs. max.
Armament: Six .50–cal. machine guns, 25 five–inch rockets, and 4,000 lbs. of bombs
Engines: Two Packard V–1650s of 1,380 hp. ea.
Cost: $228,000

PERFORMANCE

Maximum speed: 482 mph.
Cruising speed: 280 mph.
Range: 2,200 miles
Service ceiling: 39,000 ft.

SPECIFICATIONS

Span: 38 ft. 10 1/2 in.
Length: 34 ft. 6 in.
Height: 11 ft. 4 in.
Weight: 16,856 lbs. max.
Armament: Six .50–cal. machine guns and eight 5 in. rockets or 2,000 lbs. of bombs
Engine: Allison J33 of 5,400 lbs. thrust (w/water–alcohol injection)
Cost: $93,456

PERFORMANCE

Maximum speed: 580 mph.
Cruising speed: 437 mph.
Range: 1,090 miles
Service ceiling: 46,800 ft.

LOCKHEED F–80C "SHOOTING STAR"

The Shooting Star was the first USAF aircraft to exceed 500 mph in level flight, the first American jet airplane to be manufactured in large quantities and the first USAF jet to be used in combat. Designed in 1943, the XP–80 made its maiden flight on January 8, 1944. Several early P–80s were sent to Europe for demonstration, but WW II ended before the aircraft could be employed in combat. (The aircraft was redesignated in 1948 when "P" for "Pursuit" was changed to "F" for "Fighter.") Of 1,731 F–80s built, 798 were F–80Cs.

Although it was designed as a high–altitude interceptor, the F–80C was used extensively as a fighter–bomber in the Korean Conflict, primarily for low–level rocket, bomb and napalm attacks against ground targets. On November 8, 1950, an F–80C flown by Lt. Russell J. Brown, flying with the 16th Fighter–Interceptor Squadron, shot down a Russian–built MiG–15 in the world's first all–jet fighter air battle.

The F–80C on display is one of the few remaining Shooting Stars which flew combat missions during the Korean Conflict. It is painted in the markings of a unit to which it was assigned in 1950, the 8th Fighter–Bomber Group. After service in the Uruguayan Air Force during the 1960s, it was transferred to the USAF Museum in December 1970, where it was restored and then placed on display in 1979.

FAIRCHILD C–82A "PACKET"

The C–82 was designed to meet the need for a large capacity cargo aircraft that could load at near ground level. The single prototype first flew on September 10, 1944; deliveries began in late 1945 and ended in September 1948. Two hundred twenty–three Packets were built—all but four were –As. It was primarily used for cargo and troop transport, but it also was used for paratroop operations and towing gliders. Its capacity was 41 paratroops or 34 stretchers and it had clam–shell rear doors that allowed easy entry of trucks, tanks, artillery and other bulky cargo. Beginning in 1946, some C–82s were assigned to Tactical Air Command troop carrier squadrons and others to the Military Air Transport Service (MATS). Several were assigned to the Berlin Airlift primarily to carry assembled vehicles into the city. In 1947, Fairchild developed an improved Packet which the USAF accepted for production as the C–119. It had more powerful engines, increased cargo and weight capacity and a relocated flight deck.

The C–82A on display is painted and marked as an –A assigned to a post–WW II troop carrier squadron and carries red Arctic—high visibility—markings. It was flown to the Museum in 1988.

SPECIFICATIONS
Span: 106 ft. 6 in.
Length: 77 ft. 1 in.
Height: 26 ft. 4 in.
Weight: 54,000 lbs. loaded
Armament: None
Engines: Two Pratt & Whitney R–2800–85s of 2,100 hp. ea.
Crew: Five
Cost: $441,000

PERFORMANCE
Maximum speed: 250 mph.
Cruising speed: 162 mph.
Range: 2140 miles
Service ceiling: 27,000 ft.

CAPRONI Ca.36 BOMBER

In late 1914 Italian aeronautical engineer Gianni Caproni developed a three-engine bomber, the Ca.31 powered by three Gnome rotary engines. The following year Caproni produced a new version — the Ca.32. It was very similar to the Ca.31 but with three Fiat 100 horsepower water-cooled in-line engines.

Three months after Italy's entry into WW I, the first Ca.32s attacked an Austrian airbase and by the end of the year regular raids were being mounted against other Austrian targets. Caproni continued to refine his successful design with the introduction of the Isotta–Fraschini powered Ca.33. The Isottas produced 150 horsepower and were generally more reliable than the Fiats. Toward the end of the war the definitive version, the Ca.36, went into production.

The Ca.36 on display was obtained in 1987. It was restored at the Museum and was on loan from the Museo Aeronautica Caproni di Taliedo in Italy. An agreement was completed in 1994 turning ownership of the bomber over to the Air Force Museum.

SPECIFICATIONS

Span: 74 ft. 7 in.   **Length:** 36 ft. 3 in.   **Height:** 12 ft. 7 in.
Fuel capacity: 166 gallons   **Weight (loaded):** 8820 lbs.
Armament: Two Revelli 6.5mm machine guns

Bomb load: 1764 lbs.
Engines: Three Isotta–Fraschini V.4B 150 hp. water–cooled, 6–cyl.
Crew: Four

PERFORMANCE

Maximum speed: 87 mph.
Range: 372 miles
Service ceiling: 14,765 ft.

CLASSIC BOMBERS

DeHAVILLAND DH-4

The DH-4 was an ever-present element of the U.S. Army Air Service during and following WWI. When the U.S. entered WWI in April 1917, the Aviation Section of the Signal Corps only had 132 aircraft, all obsolete. Modeled from a combat-tested British DeHavilland design, the DH-4 was the only U.S.-built aircraft to see combat during WWI. With inadequate funding to buy new aircraft, the newly created U.S. Army Air Service continued to use the DH-4 in a number of roles during the lean years following the war.

During WWI, the Air Service used the DH-4 primarily for day bombing, observation, and artillery spotting. The first American-built DH-4 arrived in France in May 1918, and the 135th Aero Squadron flew the first DH-4 combat mission in early August. A total of 1,213 DH-4s were delivered to France by the war's end.

The reproduction DH-4B on display at the U.S. Air Force Museum is marked as a photographic aircraft used by the 12th Aero Squadron in 1920 to take pictures of the U.S.-Mexico border and potential emergency landing fields.

SPECIFICATIONS

Span: 43 ft. 6 in.　**Length:** 30 ft. 6 in.
Height: 10 ft. 4 in.　**Weight:** 3,557 lbs. loaded
Engine: 400 hp Liberty 12

Armament: Two .30 cal Marlin machine guns in the nose and two .30 cal. Lewis machine guns in the rear; 322 lbs of bombs

PERFORMANCE

Maximum speed: 128 mph.
Cruising speed: 90 mph.
Range: 400 miles
Service ceiling: 19,600 ft.

CLASSIC BOMBERS

MARTIN MB-2 (NBS-1) BOMBER

The Martin MB-2 was the first US designed bomber produced in large numbers. First ordered in June 1920, it replaced the handful of British Handley-Page 0-400 and Italian Caproni bombers produced in the U.S.

Designed as a night bomber, the MB-2 sacrificed speed and maneuverability to carry a heavy bomb load. Although it was more capable than the aircraft it replaced, the MB-2 reflected conventional features of the time with its internal wood structure and fabric covering. It also used the same Liberty engines used in many post World War One era aircraft.

Martin bombers were important in the history of strategic bombing since they were used by General Billy Mitchell in the bombing trials held off the Virginia coast in July of 1921. During those trials, Martin bombers sank several ships including the captured German battleship *Ostfriesland*, demonstrating the vulnerability of naval ships to aerial attack.

The MB-2 became the Air Service's and later the Air Corps' primary multi-engine bomber until replaced by the Keystone bombers in the late 1920s. The reproduction on display was completed in 2002.

SPECIFICATIONS

Span: 74 ft. 2 in. **Length:** 42 ft. 8 in. **Engine:** Two 410 hp Liberty 12 engines
Height: 14 ft. 8 in. **Weight:** 12,027 lbs. loaded **Crew:** 4
Armament: Five .30 cal machine guns, 3000 lbs of bombs

PERFORMANCE

Maximum speed: 99 mph.
Cruising speed: 91 mph.
Range: 558 miles
Service ceiling: 7700 ft.

CLASSIC BOMBERS

BOEING B–17G "FLYING FORTRESS"

The Flying Fortress is one of the most famous airplanes ever built. Few B–17s were in service on December 7, 1941, but production quickly accelerated. The aircraft served in every WWII combat zone, but is best known for daylight strategic bombing of German industrial targets. Production ended in May 1945 and totaled 12,726.

In March 1944 this B–17G was assigned to the 91st Bomb Group and based at Bassingbourn, England. There it was named *Shoo Shoo Shoo Baby* by its crew, after a popular song. It flew 24 combat missions in WW II, receiving flak damage seven times. Its first mission (Frankfurt, Germany) was on March 24, 1944, and last mission (Posen, Poland) on May 29, 1944, when engine problems forced a landing in neutral Sweden where the airplane and crew were interned. In 1968, *Shoo Shoo Shoo Baby* was found abandoned in France; the French government presented the airplane to the USAF. In July 1978 the 512th Military Airlift Wing moved it to Dover AFB, Delaware, for restoration by the volunteers of the 512th Antique Restoration Group. The aircraft was flown to the Museum in October 1988.

SPECIFICATIONS

Span: 103 ft. 10 in. **Length:** 74 ft. 4 in.
Height: 19 ft. 1 in. **Weight:** 55,000 lbs. loaded
Armament: Thirteen .50–cal. machine guns with bomb load of 6,000 lbs.
Engines: Four Wright "Cyclone" R–1820s of 1,200 hp. ea. **Cost:** $276,000

PERFORMANCE

Maximum speed: 300 mph.
Cruising speed: 170 mph.
Range: 1,850 miles
Service ceiling: 35,000 ft.

CLASSIC BOMBERS

CONSOLIDATED B–24D "LIBERATOR"

The B–24 was used in every combat theater of operations during WW II. Its excellent range made it particularly suited for such missions as the famous raid from North Africa against the oil industry at Ploesti, Romania on August 1, 1943. This feature also made the airplane suitable for long over–water missions in the Pacific Theater. More than 18,000 Liberators were built before production ended in 1945.

The B–24D on display flew combat missions from North Africa in 1943–44 with the 512th Bomb Squadron. In less than nine months, this Liberator flew 59 combat missions, receiving damage—sometimes heavy—from flak or enemy aircraft on at least nine of them. It is the same type airplane as the "Lady Be Good," the world–famous B–24D which disappeared on a mission from North Africa in April 1943 and found in the Libyan Desert in May 1959.

This combat veteran was flown to the U.S. Air Force Museum in May 1959.

SPECIFICATIONS

Span: 110 ft. 0 in.   **Length:** 66 ft. 4 in.
Height: 17 ft. 11 in.   **Weight:** 56,000 lbs. loaded
Armament: Ten .50–cal. machine guns and 8,000 lbs. of bombs
Engines: Four Pratt & Whitney R–1830s of 1,200 hp. ea.
Crew: 10   **Cost:** $336,000

PERFORMANCE

Maximum speed: 303 mph.
Cruising speed: 175 mph.
Range: 3,200 miles
Service ceiling: 28,000 ft.

CLASSIC BOMBERS

NORTH AMERICAN B–25B "MITCHELL"

The B–25 medium bomber was one of America's most famous airplanes of WW II. It was the type used by General Doolittle for the "Tokyo Raid" on April 18, 1942. Subsequently, it saw duty in every combat area being flown by the Dutch, British, Chinese, Russians and Australians in addition to our own U.S. forces. Although the airplane was originally intended for level bombing from medium altitudes, it was used extensively in the Pacific area for bombing Japanese airfields from treetop level and for strafing and skip bombing enemy shipping.

More than 9,800 B–25s were built during WW II. The airplane on display was rebuilt by North American to the configuration of the B–25B used on the Tokyo Raid and was flown to the Air Force Museum in April 1958.

SPECIFICATIONS

Span: 67 ft. 7 in. **Length:** 52 ft. 11 in.
Height: 15 ft. 9 in. **Weight:** 28,460 lbs. loaded
Armament: Five .50–cal. machine guns; 5,000 lbs. of bombs
Engines: Two Wright R–2600s of 1,700 hp. ea.
Cost: $96,000

PERFORMANCE

Maximum speed: 275 mph.
Cruising speed: 230 mph.
Range: 1,200 miles
Service ceiling: 25,000 ft.

MARTIN B–26G "MARAUDER"

Although the Marauder did not make its first flight until November 25, 1940, its design showed such promise that 1,131 B–26s were ordered by the Air Corps in September 1940. The airplane began flying combat missions in the Southwest Pacific in the spring of 1942, but most of the B–26s subsequently assigned to operational theaters were sent to England and the Mediterranean area.

Bombing from medium altitudes of 10,000 to 15,000 feet, the Marauder had the lowest loss rate of any Allied bomber—less than one-half of one percent. By the end of WW II, it had flown more than 110,000 sorties and had dropped 150,000 tons of bombs, and had been used in combat by British, Free French, Australian, South African and Canadian forces in addition to U.S. units. In 1945 when B–26 production was halted, 5,266 had been built.

The Marauder on display was flown in combat by the Free French during the final months of WW II. It was obtained from Air France's training school near Paris in June 1965.

SPECIFICATIONS

Span: 71 ft. 0 in.
Height: 20 ft. 3 in.
Armament: Eleven .50–cal. machine guns; 4,000 lbs. of bombs

Length: 58 ft. 6 in.
Weight: 37,000 lbs. loaded

Engines: Two Pratt & Whitney R–2800s of 2,000 hp. ea.
Cost: $227,000

PERFORMANCE

Maximum speed: 285 mph.
Cruising speed: 190 mph.
Range: 1,100 miles
Service ceiling: 19,800 ft.

CLASSIC BOMBERS

BOEING B–29 "SUPERFORTRESS"

The Boeing B–29 was designed in 1940 as a replacement for the B–17 and B–24. The first one built made its maiden flight on September 21, 1942. In December 1943 it was decided not to use the B–29 in the European Theater, thereby permitting the airplane to be sent to the Pacific area, where its great range made it particularly suited for the long over–water flights required to attack the Japanese homeland from bases in China. During the last two months of 1944, B–29s began operating against Japan from the islands of Saipan, Guam and Tinian.

With the advent of the conflict in Korea in June 1950, the B–29 was once again thrust into battle. For the next several years it was effectively used for attacking targets in North Korea.

The B–29 on display, named *Bockscar*, was flown to the U.S. Air Force Museum on September 26, 1961. It is the airplane that dropped the second atomic bomb on Nagasaki on August 9, 1945.

SPECIFICATIONS

Span: 141 ft. 3 in.   **Length:** 99 ft.
Height: 27 ft. 9 in.   **Weight:** 133,500 lbs. max.
Engines: Four Wright R–3350s of 2,200 hp. ea.

Armament: Eight .50–cal. machine guns in remote–controlled turrets plus two .50–cal. machine guns and one 20mm cannon in tail; 20,000 lbs. of bombs

PERFORMANCE

Maximum speed: 357 mph.
Cruising speed: 220 mph.
Range: 3,700 miles
Service ceiling: 33,600 ft.

CLASSIC BOMBERS

BOEING RB–47H "STRATOJET"

During the early Cold War, the U.S. Air Force needed an aircraft to gather information about Soviet air defense radar systems. The electronic reconnaissance RB-47H, developed from the B-47E, met this requirement. Boeing completed the first RB-47H in 1955. Boeing produced 32 new-build RB-47Hs and converted three B-47Es to become ERB-47Hs.

The RB-47H entered service in 1955 and for the next decade, crews of the 55th Strategic Reconnaissance Wing (SRW) flew it on thousands of dangerous "ferret" missions. Flying in radio silence at night along, and sometimes over, the border of the Soviet Union and other communist nations, the RB-47H crews collected essential intelligence about the size and capability of Soviet air defense radar networks.

The Museum's RB-47H was delivered to the USAF in October 1955 and served with the 55th SRW until its retirement in 1966. The aircraft came to the Museum in 1998, and after extensive restoration by Museum personnel, it went on display in 2003, marked as it appeared in 1960.

SPECIFICATIONS

Span: 116 ft.   **Length:** 107 ft. 1 in.
Height: 28 ft.   **Weight:** 226,000 lbs. max.

Armament: Two M–24 20mm cannons in tail turret plus bombs—nuclear or 10,000 lbs. of conventional bombs (not carried in RB-47H model)

PERFORMANCE

Maximum speed: 610 mph.
Cruising speed: 560 mph.
Range: 3,500 miles
Service ceiling: 39,300 ft.

CLASSIC BOMBERS

BOEING B–52D "STRATOFORTRESS"

Since it became operational in 1955, the B–52 has been the main long–range heavy bomber of the Strategic Air Command. It first flew on April 15, 1952. Nearly 750 B–52s were built when production ended in 1962. D models were modified to carry conventional bombs externally and later to carry Hound Dog missiles and Quail decoy missiles.

The B–52 has set many records in its 50–plus years of service. In 1957, three B–52Bs completed the world's first non–stop round–the–world flight by jet aircraft. It was also a B–52 that made the first airborne hydrogen bomb drop over Bikini Atoll in 1956. In June 1965, B–52s entered combat when they began flying missions with conventional bombs in support of operations in Southeast Asia (SEA).

The aircraft on display saw extensive service in SEA and was severely damaged by an enemy surface–to–air missile (SAM) on April 9, 1972. In December 1972, after being repaired, it flew four additional missions over North Vietnam. This aircraft was flown to the USAF Museum in November 1978.

SPECIFICATIONS

Span: 185 ft.　　**Length:** 156 ft. 6 in.
Height: 48 ft. 4 in.　　**Weight:** 450,000 lbs. max.
Armament: Four .50–cal. machine guns in tail plus bombs—nuclear or 43,000 lbs. of conventional

Engines: Eight Pratt & Whitney J57s of 12,100 lbs. thrust each w/water–alcohol injection

PERFORMANCE

Maximum speed: 638 mph.
Cruising speed: 526 mph.
Range: 8,338 miles
Service ceiling: 49,400 ft.

CLASSIC BOMBERS

CONVAIR B–58A "HUSTLER"

The delta-wing Hustler was the first USAF supersonic operational bomber. The B–58 made its initial flight on November 11, 1956 and flew supersonically on December 30, 1956. Distinctive B–58 features included its sophisticated inertial guidance navigation and bombing system, slender "wasp–waist" fuselage, and extensive use of heat–resistant honeycomb sandwich skin panels in the wings and fuselage. The thin fuselage prevented internal carriage of bombs so an external droppable two-component pod beneath the fuselage contained extra fuel and a nuclear weapon, reconnaissance equipment, or other specialized gear.

The USAF ordered 136 Hustlers which were operational with the Strategic Air Command between 1960 and 1970. B–58s set 19 world speed and altitude records and won five different aviation trophies.

The B–58A on display flew from Los Angeles to New York and return on March 5, 1962, setting three separate speed records and earning the crew the Bendix and Mackay Trophies for 1962. It was flown to the Museum in December 1969.

SPECIFICATIONS

Span: 56 ft. 10 in.   **Length:** 96 ft. 10 in.
Height: 31 ft. 5 in.   **Weight:** 163,000 lbs.
Armament: One 20mm cannon in tail;
nuclear weapons in pod or on pylons

Engine: J79s of 15,500 lbs. thrust each
with afterburner
Crew: 3
Cost: $12,442,000

PERFORMANCE

Maximum speed: 1,325 mph.
Cruising speed: 610 mph.
Range: 4,400 miles
Service ceiling: 64,800 ft.

CLASSIC BOMBERS

BOEING B-1B "LANCER"

The B-1B is the improved variant of the B-1A, which was cancelled in 1977. The program was resurrected in 1981 with the first production model flying in 1984. The first operational B-1B was delivered to the Air Force in 1985.

The B-1B's blended wing/body configuration, variable-geometry design, and turbofan engines combine to provide great range and high speed — more than 900 mph at sea level. Forward wing settings are used for takeoffs, landings, and high-altitude maximum cruise. Sweptwing settings are used in high subsonic and supersonic flight and also enhance the B-1B's maneuverability.

The B-1B employs forward-looking radar and terrain-following radar. Its extremely accurate Global Positioning System/Inertial Navigation System, Doppler radar, and radar altimeter enable aircrews to navigate around the world without ground-based navigation aids.

The Museum's aircraft from the 7th Bomb Wing, Dyess AFB, Texas, arrived on September 10, 2002.

SPECIFICATIONS
Length: 146 ft.   **Height:** 34 ft.
Armament: Up to 84 Mk-82 GPU bombs or 30 CBU-87/89 cluster bombs or 24 GBU-31 JDAMs

Engines: Four General Electric F101–GE–102 afterburning turbofans of 30,000 lbs. thrust each.
Crew: Four

PERFORMANCE
Maximum speed: 1,390 mph.
Cruising speed: 647 mph.
Range: 6,100 miles

CLASSIC CARGO PLANES

CURTISS C–46D "COMMANDO"

The C–46 was developed from the new and unproven commercial aircraft design, the CW–20, which first flew in March 1940. Deliveries of AAF C–46s began in July 1942. During WW II, the AAF accepted 3,144 C–46s for hauling cargo and personnel and for towing gliders. Of this total, 1,410 were C–46Ds. The C–46 gained its greatest fame during WWII transporting war materials over the "Hump" from India to China after the Japanese had closed the Burma Road. C–46 flights on this treacherous air route over the Himalayas began in May 1943. The Commando carried more cargo than the famous C-47 and offered better performance at higher altitudes, but under these difficult flying conditions, C–46s required extensive maintenance and had a relatively high loss rate. In Europe, C–46s dropped paratroopers during the aerial crossing of the Rhine River near Wesel in March 1945. C–46s saw additional service during the Korean Conflict.

The C–46D on display is painted as a C–46 flying the Hump in 1944. This aircraft was retired from USAF service in Panama in 1968 and was flown to the Museum in 1972.

SPECIFICATIONS
Span: 108 ft. 0 in. **Length:** 76 ft. 4 in.
Height: 22 ft. 0 in. **Weight:** 51,000 lbs. max.
Engines: Two Pratt & Whitney R–2800s of 2,000 hp. ea.
Cost: $233,000

PERFORMANCE
Maximum speed: 245 mph.
Cruising speed: 175 mph.
Range: 1,200 miles
Service ceiling: 27,600 ft.

CLASSIC CARGO PLANES

DOUGLAS C–47D "SKYTRAIN"

Few aircraft are as well known or were so widely used for so long as the C–47 or "Gooney Bird" as it was affectionately nicknamed. The aircraft was adapted from the DC–3 commercial airliner which appeared in 1936. The first C–47s were ordered in 1940, and by the end of WW II 9,348 had been procured for AAF use. They carried personnel and cargo, and in a combat role, towed troop–carrying gliders and dropped paratroops into enemy territory.

After WW II, many C–47s remained in USAF service, participating in the Berlin Airlift and other peacetime activities. During the Korean Conflict, C–47s hauled supplies, dropped paratroops, evacuated wounded and dropped flares for night bombing attacks. In Southeast Asia, the C–47 served again as a transport, but it was also used in a variety of other ways which included flying ground attack (gunship), reconnaissance, and psychological warfare missions.

The C–47D on display, the last C–47 in routine USAF use, was flown to the Museum in 1975. It is displayed as a C–47A of the 88th Troop Carrier Squadron, 438th Troop Carrier Group, which participated in the D-Day invasion.

SPECIFICATIONS

Span: 95 ft.   **Length:** 64 ft. 5 in.   **Height:** 16 ft. 11 in.
Weight: 33,000 lbs. loaded
Engines: Two Pratt & Whitney R–1830s of 1,200 hp. each.
Crew: Six   **Cost:** $138,000

PERFORMANCE

Maximum speed: 232 mph.
Cruising speed: 175 mph.
Range: 1,513 miles
Service ceiling: 24,450 ft.

CLASSIC CARGO PLANES

FAIRCHILD C–119J "FLYING BOXCAR"

The C–119 was designed to carry cargo, personnel, litter patients, and mechanized equipment, and to drop cargo and troops by parachute. The first C-119 made its initial flight in November 1947, and by the time production ceased in 1955, more than 1,100 C–119s had been built. The USAF used the airplane extensively during the Korean War, and many were supplied to the U.S. Navy and Marine Corps and to the air forces of Canada, Belgium, Italy, and India. In South Vietnam, the airplane once again entered combat, this time in a ground support role as AC–119 "gunships," mounting side–firing weapons capable of firing up to 6,000 rounds per minute per gun.

The C–119J on display was specially modified for the mid–air retrieval of space capsules re–entering the atmosphere from orbit. On August 19, 1960, this aircraft made the world's first mid–air recovery of a capsule returning from space when it "snagged" the parachute lowering the Discoverer XIV satellite at 8,000 feet altitude 360 miles southwest of Hawaii. The airplane was delivered to the Museum in November 1963.

SPECIFICATIONS

Span: 109 ft. 3 1/4 in. **Length:** 86 ft. 5 3/4 in.
Height: 26 ft. 7 3/4 in. **Weight:** 66,900 lbs. max.
Engines: Two Wright R–3350s of 3,500 hp. each.
Cost: $590,000

PERFORMANCE

Maximum speed: 290 mph.
Cruising speed: 200 mph.
Range: 2,000 miles
Service ceiling: 30,000 ft.

CLASSIC CARGO PLANES

DOUGLAS C–124C "GLOBEMASTER II"

The C–124 evolved from the earlier Douglas C–74. To facilitate cargo handling, the C–124, or "Old Shakey" as it was affectionately known, featured "clamshell" loading doors and hydraulic ramps in the nose and an elevator under the aft fuselage. It was capable of handling such bulky cargo as tanks, field guns, bulldozers, and trucks. It also could be converted into a transport capable of carrying 200 fully–equipped soldiers in its double–decked cabin.

The first flight by a C–124 took place on November 27, 1949 and deliveries of C–124As began in May 1950. The USAF bought 448 C–124s before production ended in 1955. These planes performed such missions as airlift support in the Far East and Southeast Asia, resupply missions to Antarctica, refugee evacuation in the Congo and mercy flights throughout the world following floods and other natural disasters.

The aircraft on display is marked as a C–124 assigned to the 909th Military Airlift Group making supply runs to Southeast Asia in the late 1960s and early 1970s.

SPECIFICATIONS

Span: 174 ft. 1 in. **Length:** 130 ft.
Height 48 ft. 4 in. **Weight:** 216,000 lbs. max.
Engines: Four Pratt & Whitney R-4360s of 3,800 hp each

PERFORMANCE

Maximum Speed: 320 mph
Cruising Speed: 200 mph
Range: 2,175 miles
Service Ceiling: 34,000 ft

SPECIFICATIONS

Main rotor diameter: 48 ft.
Tail rotor diameter: 8 ft. 5 in.
Height: 12 ft. 11 in.
Fuselage length: 41 ft. 2 in.
Weight: 4,815 lbs. loaded
Armament: None
Engine: Pratt & Whitney
R–985 of 450 hp.

PERFORMANCE

Maximum speed: 90 mph.
Cruising speed: 70 mph.
Range: 280 miles
Service ceiling: 10,000 ft.

SIKORSKY YH–5A "DRAGON FLY"

The H–5, originally designated the R–5 (H for helicopter; R for rotorcraft), was designed to provide a helicopter having greater useful load, endurance, speed, and service ceiling than the R–4. The first XR–5 of four ordered made its initial flight on August 18, 1943. In March 1944, the AAF ordered 26 YR–5As for service testing, and in February 1945, the first YR–5A was delivered.

During its service life, the H–5 was used for rescue and mercy missions throughout the world. It gained its greatest fame, however, during the Korean Conflict when it was called upon repeatedly to rescue United Nations' pilots shot down behind enemy lines and to evacuate wounded personnel from frontline areas.

More than 300 H–5s had been built by the time production was halted in 1951. The YH–5A on display, one of the 26 ordered in 1944, was obtained from Eglin AFB, Florida, in March 1955.

LOCKHEED P–80R "SHOOTING STAR"

After the end of World War II, the AAF's quest for the world's speed record, then held by a British Gloster Meteor, brought about the creation of this specialized airplane, the P–80R. It is a high–speed variant of the standard P–80A Shooting Star, but with a smaller canopy, redesigned air intakes, and a shorter wing with an extended leading edge. In addition, the engine has been modified, the armament removed and replaced by a fuel tank, and all drag–producing openings sealed. On June 19, 1947, at Muroc Army Air Field (now Edwards AFB), California, Col. Albert Boyd flew the P–80R to a new world's speed record of 623.753 mph, returning the record to the U.S. after nearly 24 years.

The P–80R is a descendant of the original Shooting Star, the XP–80, which, in 1943, was designed and built in only 143 days by a special team headed by Lockheed's Chief Research Engineer, Clarence L. "Kelly" Johnson. First flown on January 8,1944, the XP–80 was the first American airplane able to sustain speeds in excess of 500 mph in level flight. Although WW II ended before any P–80s reached combat, the Shooting Star became the first American jet to enter large–scale production.

The P–80R on display is the only one built. It was shipped to the Museum from Griffiss AFB, New York, in October 1954.

SPECIFICATIONS

Span: 37 ft.
Length: 34 ft. 6 in.
Height: 11 ft. 4 in.
Weight: 12,504 lbs. max.
Armament: None
Engine: Modified Allison J33–A–21 of 5,790 lbs. thrust (with alcohol–water injection)
Crew: One
Cost: $168,000

PERFORMANCE

Maximum speed: 623.753 mph.
Range: 1,045 miles
Service ceiling: 45,000 ft.

SPECIFICATIONS

Span: 230 ft.
Length: 162 ft. 1 in.
Height: 46 ft. 9 in.
Weight: 410,000 lbs. loaded
Armament: Sixteen M24 20mm cannons in eight nose, tail, and fuselage turrets; plus bombs—nuclear or 86,000 lbs. of conventional
Engines: Six Pratt & Whitney R–4360s of 3,800 hp. ea. and four General Electric J47s of 5,200 lbs. thrust ea.
Cost: $3,701,000

PERFORMANCE

Maximum speed: 435 mph.
Cruising speed: 230 mph.
Range: 10,000 miles
Service ceiling: 45,700 ft.

CONVAIR B–36J

The B–36, an intercontinental bomber, was designed during WW II. The airplane made its maiden flight on August 8, 1946 and on June 26, 1948 the Strategic Air Command received its first B–36 for operational use. By August 1954, when production ended, more than 380 B–36s had been built for the USAF.

In 1958–59, the B–36 was replaced by the more modern B–52. During the years it was in service, the airplane was one of America's major deterrents to aggression by a potential enemy. The fact that the B–36 was never used in combat was indicative of its value in "keeping the peace."

The Museum's B–36J was flown to Wright Field from Davis–Monthan AFB, Arizona, on April 30, 1959. This was the last flight ever made by a B–36. It was also the first airplane to be placed inside the new Museum building where it remained until moved to the Museum's new Cold War Gallery in 2003.

NORTH AMERICAN B–45C "TORNADO"

The B–45 was the first American four–engine jet bomber to fly and the first USAF jet bomber to go into production. Work on the design of the "Tornado" began during WW II and the first B–45 made its initial flight on March 17, 1947. B–45s remained operational in the USAF from 1948 until 1958.

North American built a total of 142 B–45s including 10 long–range B–45Cs with wingtip fuel tanks and 33 RB–45Cs configured for high altitude photo reconnaissance. Some RB–45Cs flew combat missions during the Korean Conflict.

In 1952, using in–flight refueling, two RB–45Cs made the first nonstop trans–Pacific flight by multi–engine jet bombers. In flying the 3,640 miles from Alaska to Japan in 9 hours and 50 minutes, one of the pilots won the Mackay Trophy for the most meritorious flight of that year.

The aircraft on display was returned to the USAF by Pratt & Whitney to which it had been on loan for engine testing purposes. It was flown to the Museum in 1971. It is painted in the markings of the 47th Bomb Group (Light) based in England in 1952-55.

SPECIFICATIONS

Span: 89 ft.
Length: 75 ft. 4 in.
Height: 25 ft. 2 in.
Weight: 110,050 lbs. max.
Armament: Two .50–cal. machine guns in the tail; 22,000 lbs. of bombs
Engines: Four General Electric J47s of 6,000 lbs. thrust each
Cost: $1,081,000

PERFORMANCE

Maximum speed: 570 mph.
Cruising speed: 500 mph.
Range: 1,000 miles
Service ceiling: 37,550 ft.

SPECIFICATIONS

Span: 28 ft.
Length: 35 ft. 7 in.
Height: 10 ft. 8 in.
Weight: 16,590 lbs. loaded
Armament: None
Engine: Reaction Motors XLR–11–RM–6 four–chamber rocket engine of 6,000 lbs. thrust.

PERFORMANCE

Maximum speed: 1,650 mph.
Landing speed: 170 mph.
Maximum altitude: 90,000 ft.

BELL X–1B

The X–1B was one of a series of rocket–powered experimental research airplanes designed for investigation of various problems associated with supersonic flight. Specifically, the mission of the X–1B was flight research pertaining to aerodynamic heating and pilot reaction control systems. It made its first powered flight on October 8, 1954.

On all test missions, the X–1B was carried to launching altitude, normally 25,000 to 35,000 feet, nestled under a "mother" airplane. It was then released in mid–air and rocket power was applied which, under full throttle, lasted less than five minutes. After all fuel (an alcohol–water mixture) and liquid oxygen had been consumed, the pilot glided the airplane to earth for landing.

The airplane on display was transferred to the U.S. Air Force Museum in January 1959.

REPUBLIC F–84E "THUNDERJET"

The F–84, the USAF's first post–war fighter, made its initial flight on February 28, 1946. It began rolling off the production lines in June 1947, and by the time production ceased in 1953, approximately 4,450 "straight–wing" F–84s (in contrast to the swept–wing F–84F) had been built. In addition to being used by the USAF, many were supplied to allied nations participating in the Mutual Security Program. During its service life, the F–84 became the first USAF jet fighter able to carry a tactical atomic weapon.

The airplane gained its greatest renown during the Korean Conflict where it was used primarily for low–level interdiction missions. Almost daily F–84s attacked enemy railroads, bridges, supply depots and troop concentrations with bombs, rockets and napalm.

The F–84E on display was obtained from Robins AFB, Georgia, in October 1963.

SPECIFICATIONS

Span: 36 ft. 5 in.
Length: 38 ft. 6 in.
Height: 12 ft. 7 in.
Weight: 15,227 lbs. loaded
Armament: Six .50–cal. machine guns and eight 5 in. rockets or 2,000 lbs. of bombs or napalm tanks
Engine: Allison J35 of 4,900 lbs. thrust
Cost: $212,000

PERFORMANCE

Maximum speed: 620 mph.
Cruising speed: 485 mph.
Range: 1,485 miles
Service ceiling: 43,240 ft.

SPECIFICATIONS

Span: 33 ft. 7 in.
Length: 42 ft. 11 in.
Height: 14 ft. 4in.
Weight: 17,000 lbs.
Armament: Four .50-cal. machine guns
Engine: Allison J35-A-25 jet engine of 5,200 lbs. thrust (later F-84Fs used Wright J-65 jet engines of 7220 lbs. thrust)
Crew: One

PERFORMANCE

Maximum speed: 670 mph.
Cruising speed: 600 mph.
Range: 1,800 statute miles
Service ceiling: 45,000 ft.

REPUBLIC YRF-84F "FICON"

The YRF-84F was the prototype of the standard USAF F-84F "Thunderstreak." Originally designated the YF-96A, it consisted of an F-84E "Thunderjet" fuselage with swept-back wings and tail. As the YF-96A, it made its initial flight on 3 June, 1950.

During the early 1950s the Air Force decided to conduct experiments on the feasibility of B-36s carrying fighter aircraft suspended under their bellies. This would not only provide the bomber with its own fighter protection, but would make it possible for the bomber to carry the fighter long distances to a combat zone. Upon reaching the edge of an enemy's territory, the fighter would be released so it could continue on its own to conduct reconnaissance or bombing missions.

The YF-96A, redesignated the YRF-84F "FICON" (contraction of Fighter and Conveyor), was modified so that it could be carried by a B-36. As the FICON, it made its first flight on 30 March 1953. Twenty-Five RF-84Fs were modified to become RF-84K FICON reconnaissance aircraft and were assigned to one Strategic Squadron where they were teamed with RB-36Ds fitted with retractable cradles to launch and recover the FICON aircraft. The unit was in existence until 1956. Subsequent development of mid-air refueling for range extension of fighter aircraft proved so successful that experiments with parasite fighters were discontinued.

MIKOYAN–GUREVICH MiG–15 "FAGOT"

The MiG–15 was developed by the Soviet Union following WW II. It began appearing in service in 1949, and by 1952 it had been provided to a number of Communist satellite nations, including North Korea where it was used extensively against United Nations forces.

The airplane on display was flown to South Korea on September 21, 1953 by a defecting North Korean pilot who was given a reward of $100,000. The airplane was subsequently flight–tested on Okinawa and then brought to Wright–Patterson AFB for additional flight tests. An offer by the U.S. to return the airplane to its "rightful owners" was ignored, and in November 1957 it was transferred to the U.S. Air Force Museum for public exhibition.

SPECIFICATIONS

Span: 33 ft. 1 1/2 in.
Length: 33 ft. 3 5/8 in.
Height: 11 ft. 2 in.
Weight: 11,270 lbs. max.
Armament: Two 23mm cannons and one 37mm cannon, plus rockets or 2,000 lbs. of bombs
Engine: VK–1 of 6,000 lbs. thrust (copy of British Rolls–Royce "Nene" engine)

PERFORMANCE

Maximum speed: 670 mph.
Cruising speed: 525 mph.
Range: 500 miles
Service ceiling: 51,000 ft.

SPECIFICATIONS

Span: 37 ft. 1 in.
Length: 40 ft. 4 in.
Height: 15 ft.
Weight: 19,975 lbs. loaded
Armament: Twenty–four 2.75 in. Mighty Mouse folding fin aircraft rockets
Engine: General Electric J47 of 7,650 lbs. thrust with afterburner
Crew: One
Cost: $344,000

PERFORMANCE

Maximum speed: 715 mph.
Cruising speed: 550 mph.
Range: 800 miles
Service ceiling: 50,000 ft.

NORTH AMERICAN F–86D "SABRE"

The F–86D (known briefly as the YF–95A) made its first flight on December 22, 1949. It was developed as an all–weather interceptor version of the famed F–86A, the airplane that won supremacy of the skies from the MiG 15 during the Korean Conflict. The F–86D was used during the 1950s—both in the U.S. and overseas—to guard against possible air attack. In all, 2,506 –Ds were produced.

The F–86D was known for two historic firsts. It was the first USAF airplane to have all–rocket armament, and the first all–weather interceptor to carry only one person for operating the radar fire control system as well as piloting the airplane. It also had the unique distinction of succeeding itself in setting a new world's speed record—698.505 mph on November 19, 1952 and 715.697 mph on July 16, 1953.

The aircraft on display was transferred to the Museum in August 1957. It is marked as an F–86D assigned to the 97th Fighter Interceptor Squadron at Wright–Patterson AFB during the mid–1950s.

REPUBLIC F–84F "THUNDERSTREAK"

The swept–wing F–84F evolved from the straight–wing F–84. The prototype first flew on June 3, 1950 and deliveries began in 1954, primarily to the Tactical Air Command as a ground support fighter bomber.

Republic built 2,112 "–F"s while General Motors fabricated an additional 599. Of these, 1,301 were delivered to NATO air forces. Production of a reconnaissance version, the RF–84F, totaled 718 aircraft, including 386 for allied countries. The RF–84F featured engine air intakes at the wing roots plus cameras in the nose.

F–84Fs gradually were replaced by supersonic F–100s in the late 1950s and were turned over to Air National Guard units. However, some F–84Fs were called back to temporary USAF service in the early 1960s due to the Berlin Crisis.

The aircraft on display was flown to the Museum in 1970 following its assignment to the Ohio ANG. During its career, it served in England, Greece, Alaska, and the continental U.S. It was one of the 200 fighters which participated in the mass deployment of aircraft across the Atlantic Ocean to Europe in November 1961 in response to the Berlin situation.

SPECIFICATIONS
Span: 33 ft. 7 in.
Length: 43 ft. 5 in.
Height: 15 ft.
Weight: 27,000 lbs. max.
Armament: Six .50–cal. machine guns and 24 five–inch rockets; 6,000 lbs. of bombs externally
Engine: One Wright J65 of 7,220 lbs. thrust
Cost: $769,000

PERFORMANCE
Maximum speed: 685 mph.
Cruising speed: 535 mph.
Range: 1,900 miles
Service ceiling: 44,450 ft.

SPECIFICATIONS

Span: 59 ft. 10 in.
Length: 53 ft. 8 in.
Height: 17 ft. 6 in.
Weight: 47,700 lbs. max.
Armament: Two AIR–2A Genie air–to–air rockets with nuclear warheads plus four AIM–4C Falcon missiles
Engines: Two Allison J35s of 7,200 lbs. thrust ea. with afterburner
Cost: $1,009,000

PERFORMANCE

Maximum speed: 627 mph.
Cruising speed: 465 mph.
Range: 1,600 miles
Service ceiling: 45,000 ft.

NORTHROP F–89J "SCORPION"

The F–89 was a twin–engine, all–weather fighter–interceptor designed to locate, intercept, and destroy enemy aircraft by day or night under all types of weather conditions. It carried a pilot in the forward cockpit and a radar operator in the rear who guided the pilot into the proper attack position. The first F–89 made its initial flight in August 1948 and deliveries to the Air Force began in July 1950. Northrop produced 1,050 F–89s.

On July 19, 1957, a Genie test rocket was fired from an F–89J, the first time in history that an air–to–air rocket with a nuclear warhead was launched and detonated. Three hundred and fifty F–89Ds were converted to "J" models which became the Air Defense Command's first fighter–interceptor to carry nuclear armament.

The Scorpion on display was transferred to the U.S. Air Force Museum from the Maine Air National Guard in July 1969. At the time of its transfer, it was the last F–89 aircraft remaining in service with an operational unit. It is painted as an F–89J assigned to the 449th Fighter Interceptor Squadron at Ladd AFB (Fairbanks), Alaska in the late 1950s and carries insignia red arctic markings.

REPUBLIC XF–91 "THUNDERCEPTOR"

The XF–91, a high–speed experimental interceptor, was America's first rocket–powered fighter to fly faster than the speed of sound. The airplane had a number of unusual design features—an inverse taper wing (wider at the tips than at the roots), a variable incidence wing that could be varied in flight (high angle of attack for takeoff and landing and low angle of attack for high–speed flight), a main landing gear that retracted outward with the tandem wheels being housed in the wing tips and a rocket engine that augmented the standard jet engine to provide an outstanding rate of climb.

The airplane made its first flight on May 9, 1949. Numerous other test flights were made which provided valuable research data, but the airplane was not put into production because it did not carry sufficient fuel for a flight of longer than 25 minutes, and it did not incorporate the latest type of fire control system.

The XF–91 on display was transferred to the Air Force Museum from Edwards AFB, California in May 1955.

SPECIFICATIONS

Span: 31 ft. 3 in.
Length: 43 ft. 3 in.
Height: 18 ft. 1 in.
Weight: 28,300 lbs. loaded
Armament: Four 20mm cannons
Engines: General Electric J47 of 6,700 lbs. thrust with afterburner and Reaction Motors rocket of 6,000 lbs. thrust.
Cost: $5,000,000

PERFORMANCE

Maximum Speed: 984 mph.
Cruising Speed: 560 mph.
Endurance: 25 minutes
Service ceiling: 48,700 ft.

SPECIFICATIONS

Span: 141 ft. 2 in.
Length: 117 ft. 5 in. (with boom retracted)
Height: 38 ft. 4 in.
Weight: 153,000 lbs. normal max.
Armament: None
Engines: Four Pratt & Whitney R–4360s of 3,500 hp. ea. and two General Electric J47s of 5,970 lbs. thrust ea.
Cost: $1,205,000

PERFORMANCE

Maximum speed: 400 mph.
Cruising speed: 230 mph.
Normal range: 2,300 miles
Service ceiling: 30,000 ft.

BOEING KC–97L "STRATOFREIGHTER"

The C–97 was the AAF cargo/transport version of the B–29. Between 1943 and 1950, 74 Stratofreighters were ordered; the first flight occurred on November 15, 1944. A tanker version (KC–97) was introduced in 1950 using the "flying boom" refueling system and all subsequent USAF contracts for C–97s were for tankers. In all, 890 aircraft were ordered, 74 C–97s and 816 KC–97s. After 1956 USAF KC–97s were gradually replaced by KC–135 jet tankers, but some were modified for continued use in other roles. In 1964, selected aircraft were returned to a tanker configuration (KC–97L) primarily for the Air National Guard. Two jet engines were added to increase speed and altitude, making the tankers more compatible with high performance jet aircraft. Although the last USAF C/KC–97 was retired in 1973, examples remained in use with the AF Reserve and ANG as tankers or air–sea search and rescue aircraft.

On June 7, 1973, the aircraft on display was christened "Zeppelinheim" by the mayor of that German town honoring its use by the 160th Air Refueling Group (Ohio ANG) during Operation "Creek Party," the aerial refueling of NATO forces in Europe. It was flown to the Museum in August 1976.

CONVAIR XF-92

The Convair Model 7002 was completed in 1948 as a flying mock-up for the proposed delta wing XP-92 interceptor. In 1948 the Air Force designated fighter aircraft as "F" rather than "P" for pursuit. The XP-92 was to be powered with a new propulsion system that would consist of a ramjet engine with several small rockets inside the combustion chamber. It would have been a short range Mach 1.65 interceptor with a flight time at altitude of 5.4 minutes. The Model 7002 was designed to investigate delta wing behavior at low and high subsonic speeds. When the XP-92's engine proved too impractical to build, the project was shelved in 1948. Even as the XP-92 program was ending, the Model 7002 was being prepared to fly. The 7002 was initially powered by an Allison J33-A-23 turbojet engine and later the J33-A-29 turbojet with afterburners. It was formally delivered to the Air Force on May 14, 1949 and named the XF-92. It was flown by Air Force test pilots until its nose gear collapsed on landing in 1953, ending its flying career. With the experience gained from the XF-92 program, Convair was able to win the competition for the "1954 Interceptor" program and to build the successful delta wing F-102. After being on static display at the University of the South in Sewanee, Tennessee, the XF-92 was shipped to the Air Force Museum in 1969 for restoration and display.

SPECIFICATIONS
Span: 31 ft. 3 in.
Length: 42 ft. 5 in.
Height: 17 ft. 8 in.
Weight: 8,500 lbs. empty
Armament: None
Engines: Allison J-33-A-23 with 4,200 lb thrust; J-33-A-29 with 7,500 lb thrust
Crew: One
Cost: $6,048,928

PERFORMANCE
Maximum Speed: 715 mph.
Cruising speed: 654 mph.
Range: 2,200 miles
Service ceiling: 40,000 ft.

SPECIFICATIONS
Rotor diameter: 53 ft.
Fuselage length: 42 ft. 4 in.
Height: 15 ft. 4 in.
Weight: 8,400 lbs. max.
Armament: None
Engine: Wright R–1300–3 of 700 hp.
Crew: Two
Cost: $150,000

PERFORMANCE
Maximum speed: 112 mph.
Cruising speed: 92 mph.
Range: 330 miles
Service ceiling: 15,000 ft.

SIKORSKY UH–19B "CHICKASAW"

The UH–19B is a USAF version of the Sikorsky S–55, an aircraft used by all U.S. military services in the 1950s and 1960s. It was the first of the Sikorsky helicopters with enough cabin space and lifting ability to allow satisfactory operation in troop transport or rescue roles. The engine is mounted in the nose, leaving the main cabin free for passengers or cargo. The prototype was first flown in November 1949, and in 1951 the USAF ordered production model H–19s (redesignated UH–19s in 1962). After receiving 50 H–19As, the USAF acquired 270 H–19Bs with increased engine power. Many were assigned to Air Rescue squadrons as SH–19s (later redesignated HH–19s). For rescue service, a 400 lb. capacity hoist was mounted above the door. The aircraft also could be equipped with an external sling capable of carrying 2,000 lbs. During the Korean War, H–19s were used extensively for rescue and medical evacuation work. Other missions included observation and liaison. The H–19 flew the first helicopter combat airlift missions during the Korean War while serving with the U.S. Marine Corps as the HRS.

The UH–19B on display is painted and marked as an H–19A known as "Hopalong," one of two H–19s to make the first trans–Atlantic helicopter flight, traveling during the summer of 1952 from Westover AFB, Massachusetts to Scotland in five stages.

GRUMMAN HU–16B "ALBATROSS"

The versatile "Albatross" amphibian was designed to meet a Navy requirement for a utility aircraft which could operate from land or water and, with skis, from snow and ice. The prototype first flew on October 24, 1947 and soon after the USAF ordered a quantity for air–sea rescue duties as SA–16As. (In 1962 the USAF designation was changed to HU–16.) Grumman delivered 297 "–A"s to the Air Force; most were assigned to the Air Rescue Service.

In 1955, Grumman developed an improved version with a 16 1/2 foot increase in wing span and larger aileron and tail surfaces. Beginning in 1957, many "–A"s were converted to the "–B" configuration with these improvements.

The Albatross is best known as a rescue aircraft. During the Korean Conflict, Albatrosses rescued almost 1,000 United Nations personnel from coastal waters and rivers, often behind enemy lines. They also made numerous dramatic and hazardous rescues in Southeast Asia, on occasion taxiing many miles over rough, open water when unable to take–off.

The HU–16 on display was one of the last operational USAF Albatrosses. It established a world altitude record for twin–engine amphibians when it reached 32,883 feet on July 4, 1973. Two weeks later, it was flown to the U.S. Air Force Museum .

SPECIFICATIONS
Span: 96 ft. 8 in.
Length: 62 ft. 10 in.
Height: 25 ft. 10 in.
Weight: 36,000 lbs. max.
Engines: Two Wright R–1820s of 1,425 hp. ea.
Cost: $510,000

PERFORMANCE
Maximum speed: 250 mph.
Cruising speed: 165 mph.
Range: 1,650 miles
Service ceiling: 22,000 ft.

SPECIFICATIONS

Span: 36 ft. 2 in.
Length: 27 ft. 4 in.
Height: 8 ft. 4 in.
Weight: 3,350 lbs. loaded
Armament: None
Engine: Jacobs R-755-A2 of 300 hp
Crew: One, with provisions for four passengers

PERFORMANCE

Maximum speed: 175 mph
Cruising speed: 136 mph
Range: 852 statute miles
Service ceiling: 20,000 ft.

CESSNA LC-126A

The LC-126A light utility transport is a military version of the commercial Cessna Model 195 cabin monoplane. The Model 195, which had developed a reputation for ruggedness and excellent performance, attracted the attention of the U.S. Air Force when it was looking for aircraft suitable for Arctic service. As a result, the Air Force ordered 15 LC-126As in 1948 for use in rescue operations in Alaska. The aircraft were delivered in early 1949 and each of them was provided with an interchangeable set of floats and skis to permit operation from land, snow, or water. The LC-126A is identical to the Model 195 except for the paint scheme, interior fittings, emergency escape hatch, and radio equipment. The LC-126A on display at the Air Force Museum is equipped with Edo floats and is marked as it appeared while serving with the 10th Rescue Squadron, Elmendorf Air Force Base, Alaska, in 1949.

MIKOYAN–GUREVICH MiG–17 "FRESCO"

The MiG–17 is a refined version of the famous MiG–15 of the Korean War. Although similar in appearance to the MiG–15, the MiG–17 has more sharply swept wings, an afterburner, better speed and handling characteristics and is about three feet longer. The first flight of a MiG–17 prototype took place in January 1950 and production began in late 1951. The first operational MiG–17s appeared in 1952 but were not available in sufficient quantities to take part in the Korean War. Five versions of the aircraft eventually were produced. The MiG–17 has served in the air arms of at least 20 nations throughout the world—including nations friendly to the U.S.—and was flown against U.S. aircraft during the Vietnam War. Between July 10, 1965, and February 14, 1968, USAF F–105s and F–4s downed 61 MiG–17s.

The aircraft on display was presented to the USAF Museum by the Egyptian Air Force in 1986 as a symbol of friendship and cooperation between the two nations.

SPECIFICATIONS
(Data for MiG–17F "Fresco C")
Span: 31 ft. 7 in.
Length: 36 ft. 5 in.
Height: 12 ft. 6 in.
Weight: 13,380 lbs. max.
Armament: One 37mm and two 23mm cannons in the lower nose plus 16 rockets in underwing pods or 1100 lbs. of bombs (externally)
Engine: Klimov VK–1F jet engine of 7,452 lbs. thrust w/afterburner.

PERFORMANCE
Maximum speed: 711 mph.
Cruising speed: 535 mph.
Range: 510 miles
(1,160 miles with external tanks)
Service ceiling: 57,000 ft.

SPECIFICATIONS

Span: 37 ft. 4 in.
Length: 44 ft. 6 in.
Height: 14 ft. 11 in.
Weight: 24,000 lbs. loaded
Armament: Twenty–four 2.75 in. Folding Fin Air Rockets (FFARs) in nose and twenty–four FFARs in two wing pods
Engine: Pratt & Whitney J48–P–5 or –5A of 8,750 lbs. thrust with afterburner
Crew: Two
Cost: $534,000

PERFORMANCE

Maximum speed: 640 mph.
Cruising speed: 476 mph.
Range: 1,275 miles
Service ceiling: 51,800 ft.

LOCKHEED F–94C "STARFIRE"

The F–94 series all–weather interceptors were developed from the Lockheed P–80 Shooting Star. The prototype F–94 first flew on July 1, 1949. The Starfire was subsequently produced in the –A, –B and –C series. The F–94C (originally designated F–97A) was a fundamental redesign of the F–94B and made its first flight on January 18, 1950.

Improvements in the F–94C included a higher thrust engine, single–point refueling, a redesigned wing, a sweptback horizontal stabilizer, upgraded fire-control and navigation systems and, later, mid–wing rocket pods. Twenty–four rockets were carried in the nose in a ring around the radome, shielded by retractable doors, with an additional 24 in the wing pods, if installed. The F–94C carried no guns. Starfires were employed in the air defense of the continental U.S. in the 1950s. In the F–94A form, they served as the first all–jet all–weather interceptor for the Air Defense Command. The last F–94Cs were withdrawn from the USAF service in 1959.

The aircraft on display has been painted to represent an F–94C assigned to the 60th Fighter Interceptor Squadron at Otis AFB, Massachusetts during the late 1950s.

VERTOL CH–21B "WORKHORSE"

The H–21 made its first flight in April 1952. The aircraft was originally designed by Piasecki to transport men and cargo but was later adapted for the rescue of personnel and for assault operations under combat conditions. Normally having a crew of two (pilot and copilot), the H–21 could carry either 20 fully-equipped troops or 12 litter patients.

In addition to serving with the USAF, the H–21 was supplied to the U.S. Army, the French Navy, the Royal Canadian Air Force and the West German Air Force.

The CH–21B on display was obtained from Eglin AFB, Florida in January 1965.

SPECIFICATIONS

Rotor diameter: 44 ft.
Fuselage length: 52 ft. 7 in.
Overall length: (including rotor arcs) 86 ft. 4 in.
Height: 15 ft. 4 in.
Weight: 10,223 lbs. loaded
Armament: None
Engine: Wright R–1820 of 1,425 hp.
Cost: $406,000

PERFORMANCE

Maximum speed: 132 mph.
Cruising speed: 90 mph.
Range: 400 miles
Service ceiling: 19,200 ft.

SPECIFICATIONS

Span: 32 ft. 10 in.
Length: 25 ft. 11 in.
Height: 9 ft. 7 in.
Weight: 2,900 lbs. loaded
Armament: None
Engine: Continental O–470–13 of 225 hp.
Crew: Two
Cost: $51,000

PERFORMANCE

Maximum speed: 191 mph.
Cruising speed: 173 mph.
Range: 821 miles
Service ceiling: 20,000 ft.

BEECH T–34A "MENTOR"

The T–34A was used by the USAF for primary flight training during the 1950s. The original Mentor, a Beechcraft Model 45 derived from the famous Beechcraft Bonanza, was first flown in December 1948. The first military prototype, designated YT–34 by the USAF, made its initial flight in May 1950.

After extensive testing, the USAF ordered the Mentor into production as the T–34A in early 1953. The first production T–34A was delivered to Edwards AFB in October 1953 for evaluation, and deliveries to the Air Training Command began in 1954.

The T–34A served as the standard primary trainer until the USAF introduced the Cessna T–37 jet trainer in the late 1950s. As they were replaced by the T–37, many T–34s were turned over to base Aero Clubs. In all, 450 T–34As were produced for the USAF. Three hundred fifty were built in the U.S.A. and 100 more were produced in Canada under license. In addition, two U.S. Navy versions of the Mentor were produced: the T–34B and the turboprop–powered T–34C. The Mentor also was built for the military forces of at least ten friendly foreign nations.

NORTH AMERICAN F–100D "SUPER SABRE"

Developed as a follow-on to the F-86 Sabre used in the Korean Conflict, the F-100 was the world's first production airplane capable of flying faster than the speed of sound in level flight (760 mph). The prototype, the YF-100A, made its first flight on May 25, 1953 at Edwards AFB, California. Of the 2,294 F-100s built before production ended in 1959, 1,294 were Ds. The D, which made its first flight on January 24, 1956, was the most advanced production version. Its features included the first autopilot designed for a supersonic jet and a low-altitude bombing system. The Super Sabre had its combat debut in Vietnam where it was used extensively as a fighter-bomber in ground-support missions attacking bridges, road junctions. and troop concentrations.

The aircraft on display was used by the "Thunderbirds," the official USAF Flight Demonstration Team, from 1964-68. During theat period, the team toured the Caribbean, Europe, Latin America, and nearly every state in the U.S. This F-100-D was retired from service with the 114th Tactical Fighter Group, South Dakota ANG, in 1977. It was restored by Thunderbird maintenance personnel to its original appearance as a team aircraft. It was flown to the Museum by the ANG and presented to the Museum by the Thunderbirds on July 22, 1977.

SPECIFICATIONS
Span: 38 ft. 10 in.
Length: 54 ft. 2 in.
Height: 16 ft. 2 in.
Weight: 38,048 lbs. loaded
Armament: Four M–39 20 mm cannons, two GAM-83A Bulldog missiles, four GAR-8 Sidewinder missiles, rockets, special stores, and/or a maximum of 7040 lbs of bombs.
Engine: Pratt & Whitney J-57 of 16,000 lbs. thrust w/afterburner
Cost: $704,000

PERFORMANCE
Maximum speed: 926.6 mph.
Cruising speed: 590 mph.
Range: 1,970 miles
Service ceiling: 55,000 ft.

SPECIFICATIONS

Span: 30 ft. 2 in.
Length: 40 ft. 3 in.
Height: 12 ft. 0 in.
Weight: 19,096 lbs. max.
Armament: Three NR-30 30mm cannon
Engine: Two Tumansky RD-9 turbojets with 7,165 lbs. thrust with after burner
Crew: One

PERFORMANCE

Maximum speed: 903 mph
Range: 1,243 statute miles
Service ceiling: 56,145 ft.

MIKOYAN-GUREVICH MiG-19S "FARMER"

The MiG-19 was the first production fighter produced by the Soviet Union capable of supersonic speeds in level flight. The MiG-19 prototype made its first flight in September 1953 and was placed into production in 1955. It was the Soviet Union's primary fighter during the last half of the 1950s. Possibly as many as 10,000 MiG-19s, in various versions, were built by the Soviet Union, China, Poland and Czechoslovakia. Many other countries used the MiG-19, including Cuba, North Vietnam, North Korea, Iraq and most of the Warsaw Pact nations. The Soviet Union phased out the MiG-19 in the early 1960s in favor of the more advanced MiG-21. However, the MiG-19 continued to be used by the other nations for many more years.

The Museum's MiG-19 was obtained from the 457th Tactical Evaluation Squadron based at Nellis Air Force Base, Nevada. It was placed on display in October 1994.

CONVAIR F–102A "DELTA DAGGER"

The primary mission of the F–102 was to intercept and destroy enemy aircraft. It was the world's first supersonic all–weather jet interceptor and the USAF's first operational delta–wing aircraft. The F–102 made its initial flight on October 24, 1953 and became operational with the Air Defense Command (ADC) in 1956. At the peak of deployment in the late 1950s, F–102s equipped more than 25 ADC squadrons. Convair built 1,101 F–102s, 975 of which were F–102As. The USAF also bought 111 TF–102s as combat trainers with side–by–side seating.

In a wartime situation, after electronic equipment on board the F–102 had located the enemy aircraft, the F–102's radar would guide it into position for attack. At the proper moment, the electronic fire control system would automatically fire the F–102's air–to–air rockets and missiles.

The F–102A on display served with the 57th Fighter–Interceptor Squadron in Iceland and was one of the first USAF aircraft to intercept a Soviet Tu–20 "Bear" bomber over the Arctic. The F–102A was flown to the Museum in 1971.

SPECIFICATIONS

Span: 38 ft. 1 in.
Length: 68 ft. 4 in. (including boom)
Height: 21 ft. 2 in.
Weight: 31,559 lbs. max.
Armament: 24 unguided 2.75 inch rockets and six guided missiles
Engine: One Pratt & Whitney J57 of 16,000 lbs. thrust w/afterburner
Cost: $1,184,000

PERFORMANCE

Maximum speed: 810 mph.
Cruising speed: 600 mph.
Range: 1,000 miles
Service ceiling: 55,000 ft.

SPECIFICATIONS

Span: 36 ft. 7 in.
Length: 60 ft. 10 in.
Height: 19 ft. 8 in.
Weight: 41,537 lbs. max.
Armament: Four 20mm cannons, 108 2.75 inch rockets and up to 4,000 lbs. of bombs
Engine: Pratt & Whitney J75 of 23,500 lbs. thrust (with afterburner)
Crew: One

PERFORMANCE

Maximum speed: Mach 2–plus
Cruising speed: 600 mph.
Range: 1,570 miles
Service ceiling: 48,000 ft.

NORTH AMERICAN F–107A

The F–107A was originally designed as a tactical fighter–bomber version of the F–100, with a recessed weapon bay under the fuselage. However, extensive design changes resulted in its redesignation from F–100B to F–107A before the first prototype flew. Special features included an all–moving vertical fin; a control system which permitted the plane to roll at supersonic speeds; and a system (Variable Area Inlet Duct) which automatically controlled the amount of air fed to the jet engine.

On September 10, 1956, the No. 1 F–107A made its initial flight, attaining Mach 1.03 (the speed of sound, Mach 1, is about 760 mph at sea level). The aircraft first achieved Mach 2 (twice the speed of sound) in tests on November 3rd. Three F–107As were built as prototypes and were test flown extensively, but the aircraft did not go into production, the Republic F–105 having been selected as the standard fighter–bomber for the Tactical Air Command. In late 1957, Nos. 1 and 3 were leased to the National Advisory Committee for Aeronautics for high–speed flight research.

The F–107A on display is aircraft No. 2, and its first flight was on November 28, 1956. It was used for weapons testing with both conventional and atomic bombs. On November 25, 1957, it was flown to the USAF Museum.

RYAN X–13 "VERTIJET"

The X–13 was designed to test the idea of vertical takeoff, transition to horizontal flight, and return to vertical flight for landing by jet aircraft. Equipped with a temporary tricycle landing gear, it was first flown conventionally on December 10, 1955 to test its overall aerodynamic characteristics. It was then fitted with a temporary "tail–sitting" rig and on May 28, 1956, flown from the ground in a vertical position to test its hovering qualities.

The airplane made history on April 11, 1957, when it completed its first full–cycle flight at Edwards AFB, California. It took off vertically from its mobile trailer, rose into the air, nosed over into a level attitude, and flew for several minutes. It then reversed the procedure to vertical flight and slowly descended to its trailer for a safe "landing."

The X–13 on display, one of two built, was the Vertijet which made the full–cycle flight on April 11, 1957. It was transferred to the U.S. Air Force Museum in May 1959.

SPECIFICATIONS
Span: 21 ft.
Length: 24 ft.
Height: 15 ft.
Weight: 7,200 lbs. max.
Armament: None
Engine: Rolls–Royce "Avon" of 10,000 lbs. thrust

PERFORMANCE
Maximum speed: 350 mph.
Minimum speed: 0 mph.
Service ceiling: 20,000 ft.

SPECIFICATIONS

Span: 21 ft. 11 in.
Length: 54 ft. 10 in.
Height: 13 ft. 6 in.
Weight: 27,853 lbs. max.
Armament: One M–61 20mm cannon, two air–to–air missiles; nuclear or conventional bombs
Engine: One General Electric J–79 of 15,800 lbs. thrust w/afterburner
Crew: One
Cost: $1,471,000

PERFORMANCE

Maximum speed: 1,320 mph.
Cruising speed: 575 mph.
Range: 1,250 miles
Service ceiling: 58,000 ft.

LOCKHEED F–104C "STARFIGHTER"

Designed as a supersonic air superiority fighter, the F–104 was produced in two major versions. Armed with a six–barrel M–61 20mm Vulcan cannon it served as a tactical fighter and, equipped additionally with heat–seeking Sidewinder missiles, as a day–night interceptor. Development of the F–104 began in 1952 and the first XF–104 made its initial flight in 1954. On May 18, 1958, an F–104A set a world speed record of 1,404.19 mph, and on December 14, 1959, an F–104C set a world altitude record of 103,395 feet. The Starfighter was the first aircraft to hold simultaneous official world records for speed, altitude and time–to–climb.

The USAF procured about 300 Starfighters in one– and two–seat versions. In addition, more than 1,700 F–104s were built in the U.S. and abroad under the military aid program for various nations including Canada, West Germany, Italy, Norway, the Netherlands, Belgium, Denmark, Greece, Turkey, Spain, Taiwan and Japan.

The aircraft on display served with the USAF in West Germany, Spain, Taiwan, Vietnam, Laos and Thailand. It also won the 1962 USAF "William Tell" Fighter Weapons Meet competition. It was flown to the Museum in August 1975.

CONVAIR F–106A "DELTA DART"

The F–106 all–weather interceptor was developed from the Convair F–102 "Delta Dagger." Originally designated F–102B, it was redesignated F–106 because it had extensive structural changes and a more powerful engine. The first F–106A flew on December 26, 1956, and deliveries to the Air Force began in July 1959. Production ended in late 1960 after 277 F–106As and 63 F–106Bs had been built.

The F–106 used a Hughes MA–1 electronic guidance and fire control system. After takeoff, the MA–1 could be given control of the aircraft to fly it to the proper altitude and attack position. Then it could fire the Genie and Falcon missiles, break off the attack run, and return the aircraft to the vicinity of its base. The pilot took control again for the landing.

The aircraft on display was involved in an unusual accident. During a training mission from Malmstrom AFB on February 2, 1970, it suddenly entered an uncontrollable flat spin forcing the pilot to eject. Unpiloted, the aircraft recovered on its own, apparently due to the balance and configuration changes caused by the ejection, and miraculously made a gentle belly landing in a snow–covered field near Big Sandy, Montana. After minor repairs, the aircraft was returned to service. It last served with the 49th Fighter Interceptor Squadron before being brought to the Museum in August 1986.

SPECIFICATIONS

Span: 38 ft. 4 in.
Length: 70 ft. 9 in.
Height: 20 ft. 4 in.
Armament: One AIR–2A Genie air–to–air nuclear missile and four AIM–4 Falcon air–to–air missiles.
Engine: One Pratt & Whitney J75–P–17 of 24,500 lbs. thrust w/afterburner.
Crew: One
Cost: $3,305,435

PERFORMANCE

Maximum speed: 1,525 mph.
Cruising speed: 650 mph.
Range: 1,500 miles
Service ceiling: 53,000 ft.

SPECIFICATIONS

Span: 64 ft.
Length: 65 ft. 6 in.
Height: 15 ft. 6 in.
Weight: 58,800 lbs. max.
Armament: None
Engines: Two Wright
J65–W–5s or two Buick
J65–BW–5s of 7,220 lbs.
thrust ea.
Crew: Pilot and electronic
warfare officer
Cost: $1,264,000

PERFORMANCE

Maximum speed: 570 mph.
Cruising speed: 450 mph.
Range: 2,000 miles
Service ceiling: 49,000 ft.

MARTIN EB–57B "CANBERRA"

The B–57 is a modified version of the English Electric Canberra which was first flown in Britain on May 13, 1949, and later produced for the Royal Air Force. After the Korean Conflict began in 1950, the USAF looked for a medium jet bomber to replace the aging Douglas B–26 Invader. In March 1951, the USAF contracted with the Glenn L. Martin Co. to build the Canberra in the U.S. under a licensing agreement with English Electric. The Martin–built B–57 made its first flight on July 20, 1953, and when production ended in 1959, a total of 403 Canberras had been produced for the USAF.

The aircraft on display is one of 202 B–57Bs built by Martin. In the early 1960s it was assigned to Aeronautical Systems Division at Wright–Patterson AFB as a test aircraft. In 1965 it was selected for return to combat configuration to replace combat losses in Southeast Asia. It arrived at Clark AB, Philippines on March 20, 1967 and was assigned to the 8th Bomb Squadron at Phan Rang, South Vietnam, where it flew combat missions for 2-1/2 years. Then, it was brought back to the U.S., converted to an electronic countermeasures EB–57B, and assigned to the Kansas Air National Guard (ANG) and later to the Vermont ANG. The aircraft was flown to the Museum on August 20, 1981.

LOCKHEED U–2A

The U–2 was designed and built for surveillance missions in the thin atmosphere above 55,000 feet. An unusual single–engine aircraft with sailplane–like wings, it was the product of a team headed by Clarence L. "Kelly" Johnson at Lockheed's "Skunk Works" in Burbank, California. The U–2 made its first flight in August 1955 and began operational service in 1956. Its employment was kept secret until May 1, 1960, when a civilian–piloted U–2 was downed on a non–USAF reconnaissance flight over Soviet territory.

USAF U–2s have been used for various missions. On October 14, 1962, Maj. Richard S. Heyser piloted a U–2 over Cuba to obtain the first photos of Soviet offensive missile sites. Maj. Rudolph Anderson, Jr. was killed on a similar mission eight days later when his U–2 was shot down. U–2s also have been used in mapping studies, atmospheric sampling and for collecting crop and land management photographic data for the Department of Agriculture.

The aircraft on display is the last U–2A built. During the 1960s it made 285 flights to gather data on high–altitude clear air turbulence. In the 1970s it was used to flight–test reconnaissance systems. It was delivered to the Museum in May 1980, and is painted as a typical USAF reconnaissance U–2.

SPECIFICATIONS

Span: 80 ft.
Length: 49 ft. 7 in.
Height: 13 ft.
Weight: 15,850 lbs. (17,270 lbs. with external fuel tanks)
Armament: None
Engine: Pratt & Whitney J57–P–37A of 11,000 lbs. thrust (J75–P–13 of 17,000 lbs. thrust for later models)

PERFORMANCE

Maximum speed: 494 mph.
Cruising speed: 460 mph.
Range: 2,200 miles (over 3,000 miles for later models)
Ceiling: Above 55,000 ft. (above 70,000 ft. for later models)

SPECIFICATIONS

Span: 72 ft. 6 in.
Length: 75 ft. 2 in.
Height: 23 ft. 7 in.
Weight: 91,000 lbs. max.
Armament: Two 20mm cannons in tail; 8,044 lbs. of photo flash bombs
Engines: Two Allison J71s of 10,200 lbs. thrust each
Cost: $2,334,000

PERFORMANCE

Maximum speed: 585 mph.
Cruising speed: 525 mph.
Range: 1,800 miles
Service ceiling: 43,000 ft.

DOUGLAS RB–66B "DESTROYER"

The B–66 was developed from the Navy A3D Skywarrior for USAF use as a tactical light bomber and photo reconnaissance aircraft. An RB–66A, one of five of these reconnaissance aircraft ordered as prototypes, was the first to fly on June 28, 1954. B–66s became operational in 1956; production ended in 1958. The RB–66B recon version was the first production series and totaled 155 of the 294 B–66s built.

The B–66 was the last tactical bomber built for the USAF, and only the B–66B was designed exclusively as a bomber. Others served as tactical recon aircraft while the final version, the WB–66D, was designed for electronic weather reconnaissance.

Some B–66s were modified for service in Vietnam as electronic countermeasures aircraft to confuse enemy radar defenses. The aircraft on display flew combat missions in Southeast Asia in an electronic countermeasures role. It was delivered to the Museum in 1970.

DOUGLAS C–133A "CARGOMASTER"

The turboprop C–133 was developed to fulfill USAF requirements for a large capacity, strategic cargo aircraft. "Cargomasters" went directly into production as the C–133A; no prototypes were built. The first C–133A made its initial flight on April 23, 1956. When production ended in 1961, Douglas had built 30 C–133As and 15 –Bs.

In 1958, C–133s began flying Military Air Transport Command air routes throughout the world, and two C–133s established trans–Atlantic speed records for transport aircraft on their first flights to Europe. With its rear–loading and side–loading doors, the C–133 was capable of handling a wide variety of military cargo. Most significant was its ability to transport ballistic missiles, such as the Atlas, cheaper and faster than by trailer over highways. With the development of the larger Lockheed C–5A, the C–133 left the active inventory in 1971.

The C–133A on display established a world record for propeller–driven aircraft when on December 16, 1958, it carried a cargo payload of 117,900 pounds to an altitude of 10,000 feet. It was flown to the U.S. Air Force Museum on March 17, 1971.

SPECIFICATIONS

Span: 179 ft. 8 in.
Length: 157 ft. 6 in.
Height: 48 ft. 8 in.
Weight: 282,000 lbs. max.
Armament: None
Engines: Four Pratt & Whitney T34s of 7,000 hp. ea.
Crew: Four

Cost: $9,782,000

PERFORMANCE

Maximum speed: 354 mph.
Cruising speed: 310 mph.
Range: 4,027 miles
Service ceiling: 23,300 ft.

SPECIFICATIONS

Span: 35 ft. 8 in.
Length: 27 ft.
Height: 10 ft. 5 in.
Weight: 4,830 lbs. max.
Armament: None
Engines: Two Continental O–470–Ms of 240 hp. ea.
Crew: Two (plus three passengers)
Cost: $56,000

PERFORMANCE

Maximum speed: 238 mph.
Cruising speed: 180 mph.
Range: 900 miles
Service ceiling: 22,000 ft.

CESSNA U–3A

Popularly known in the Air Force as the "Blue Canoe," the U–3 is the military version of the Cessna 310 light twin–engine transport. The prototype made its first flight on January 3, 1953. Production for the civilian market began in 1954, and in 1957, the USAF selected the aircraft for service as a light administrative, liaison, cargo, and utility transport. The Air Force eventually bought 160 of the 310s "off–the–shelf" under the original designation L–27A, later changed to U–3A. Thirty–five more were delivered in 1960–1961 as U–3Bs—all weather versions with more powerful engines, additional cabin windows, a longer nose and a swept vertical fin.

The aircraft on display is one of several USAF U–3As that were transferred to the U.S. Army.

FAIRCHILD C–123K "PROVIDER"

The "Provider" was a short–range assault transport used to airlift troops and cargo onto short runways and unprepared airstrips. Designed by the Chase Aircraft Co., the C–123 evolved from earlier designs for large assault gliders. The first prototype XC–123 made its initial flight on October 14, 1949, powered by two piston engines. A second prototype was built as the XG–20 glider. It was later test–flown, powered by four jet engines. The production version, with two piston engines, was designated the C–123B. Chase began manufacture in 1953, but the production contract was transferred to Fairchild. The first of more than 300 Fairchild–built C–123Bs entered service in July 1955. Between 1966 and 1969, 184 C–123Bs were converted to C–123Ks by adding two J85 jet engines for improved performance.

The aircraft on display entered service in 1957 as a C–123B. In 1961–72, it served in Vietnam—first as a UC–123B, then as a UC–123K—flying low–level defoliant and insecticide spray missions. During that time it received over 1,000 bullet and shrapnel hits. Its nickname, "Patches," derives from the metal patches that cover many of its battle scars. It is also decorated with seven Purple Hearts earned by crewmen wounded in the aircraft. It was flown to the Museum in June 1980.

SPECIFICATIONS

Span: 110 ft.
Length: 76 ft. 3 in.
Height: 34 ft. 6 in.
Weight: 60,000 lbs. max.
Armament: None
Engines: Two Pratt & Whitney R–2800 of 2,500 hp. each and two General Electric J85s of 2,850 lbs. thrust each
Crew: Three or four
Cost: $601,719

PERFORMANCE

Maximum speed: 240 mph.
Cruising speed: 170 mph.
Range: 1,825 miles
Service ceiling: 28,000 ft.

SPECIFICATIONS

Rotor diameter: 47 ft. 0 in.
Overall length: 47 ft. 0 in.
Height: 17 ft. 2 in.
Weight: 9,150 lbs. max.
Armament: None
Engine: Lycoming T–53 of 860 hp.
Cost: $304,000

PERFORMANCE

Maximum speed: 120 mph.
Cruising speed: 105 mph.
Range: 185 miles
Service ceiling: 25,000 ft.

KAMAN HH–43B "HUSKIE"

The "Huskie" was used primarily for crash rescue and aircraft fire–fighting. It was in use with the U.S. Navy when delivery of the H–43As to the USAF Tactical Air Command began in November 1958. Delivery of the –B series began in June 1959. In mid–1962, the USAF changed the H–43 designation to HH–43 to reflect the aircraft's rescue role. The final USAF version was the HH–43F with engine modifications for improved performance. Some –Fs were used in Southeast Asia as "aerial fire trucks" and for rescuing downed airmen in North and South Vietnam. Huskies were also flown by other nations including Iran, Colombia and Morocco.

A Huskie on rescue alert could be airborne in approximately one minute. It carried two rescuemen/fire–fighters and a fire suppression kit hanging beneath it. It often reached crashed airplanes before ground vehicles arrived. Foam from the kit plus the powerful downwash of air from the rotors were used to open a path to trapped crash victims to permit their rescue.

The HH–43B on display, one of approximately 175 –Bs purchased by the USAF, established seven world records in 1961–62 for helicopters in its class for rate of climb, altitude and distance traveled. It was assigned to rescue duty with Detachment 3, 42nd Aerospace Rescue and Recovery Squadron, Kirtland AFB, New Mexico, prior to its retirement and flight to the Museum in April 1973.

CESSNA T-37B

The T-37 is a twin-engine primary trainer used for teaching the fundamentals of jet aircraft operation and instrument, formation, and night flying. Affectionately known as the "Tweety Bird," it was the first USAF jet aircraft designed from conception as a trainer (as opposed to a modification such as the T-33). Its flying characteristics helped student pilots prepare to transition to the larger, faster T-38 "Talon" later in the pilot training program. Side-by-side seating in the T-37 makes it easier for the instructor to observe and communicate with the student.

The XT-37 prototype made its initial flight on October 12, 1954, and the preproduction T-37A first flew on September 27, 1955. Following modifications, the T-37A entered operational USAF service in 1957. In 1959, the T-37B joined the USAF. Similar to the -A, it had more powerful engines, a redesigned instrument panel and improved radio communications and navigational equipment. In time, all -As were modified to -B standards.

The T-37C, with provisions for armament and extra fuel, was built for export. Both T-37Bs and -Cs serve the air forces of several Allied nations. In all, nearly 1,300 T-37As, -Bs and -Cs were built before production ended in the late 1970s. In addition, nearly 600 A-37s—attack modifications of the T-37—were built.

The T-37B on display was flown to the Museum on October 8, 1991.

SPECIFICATIONS

Span: 33 ft. 10 in.
Length: 29 ft. 4 in.
Height: 9 ft. 5 in.
Weight: 6,580 lbs. max.
Armament: None
Engines: Two Continental J69-T-25s of 1,025 lbs. thrust ea.
Crew: Two
Cost: $166,000

PERFORMANCE

Maximum speed: 410 mph.
Cruising speed: 350 mph.
Range: 650 miles
Service ceiling: 35,000 ft.

SPECIFICATIONS

Span: 39 ft. 8 in.
Length: 69 ft. 3 in.
Height: 18 ft.
Weight: 51,000 lbs. max.
Armament: One MK–28 or MK–43 thermo-nuclear bomb
Engines: Two Pratt & Whitney J57s of 15,000 lbs. thrust each w/afterburner
Cost: $1,276,245

PERFORMANCE

Maximum speed: 1,000 mph.
Cruising speed: 550 mph.
Range: 2,060 miles
Service ceiling: 45,800 ft.

McDONNELL RF–101C "VOODOO"

The F–101 lineage included several versions: low–altitude fighter–bomber, photo–reconnaissance, two–seat interceptor and transition trainer. To accelerate production, no prototypes were built, and the first Voodoo, an F–101A, made its initial flight on September 29, 1954. When production ended in March 1961, nearly 800 Voodoos had been built. Development of the unarmed RF–101, the world's first supersonic photo–recon aircraft, began in 1956. Thirty-five RF–101As and 166 RF–101Cs were produced with many earlier single–seat Voodoos were converted to reconnaissance configuration.

The RF–101C on display participated in "Operation Sun Run," a high–speed transcontinental flight on November 16, 1957. Using air–to–air refueling, a team of Voodoos set nonstop speed records from Los Angeles to New York City and return. Capt. Ray W. Schrecengost, flying the plane on display, broke three speed records. This Voodoo flew vital low–altitude reconnaissance missions during the Cuban Missile Crisis and helped confirm that offensive missile sites in Cuba were being dismantled. It also served in Southeast Asia (SEA) with the 45th Tactical Reconnaissance Squadron, one of the first aircraft in SEA to revert to camouflage markings for combat use. It was transferred from the 186th Tactical Reconnaissance Group, Mississippi ANG, Key Field, Mississippi, to the USAF Museum on October 27, 1978.

NORTH AMERICAN T–39A "SABRELINER"

The T–39 was developed by North American Aviation, Inc. as a private venture to meet a USAF requirement for a twin jet utility trainer. The prototype T–39 made its first flight on September 16, 1958. In January 1959, the USAF placed a production order and on June 30, 1960, the first production T–39A made its initial flight. In all, 143 T–39As and 6 T–39Bs were built for the USAF. Another 62 T–39 variants were produced for the Navy. After the bulk of military contracts had been met, the Sabreliner entered the commercial market where it became a highly successful executive jet transport.

The T–39A on display was delivered to the USAF on June 6, 1963. It was transferred to Europe and flew missions there until damaged in a crash in 1966. It was repaired by the manufacturer and returned to service in August 1967. From August 1968 until early 1973, this Sabreliner was assigned to Bergstrom AFB, Texas, in support of former President Lyndon B. Johnson. After undergoing a fatigue life extension program, the aircraft was sent to Andrews AFB, Maryland, where in 1974 it began flying as a test bed for state–of–the–art avionics equipment and as an administrative airlift support transport. This T–39A was flown to the Museum on October 24, 1984.

SPECIFICATIONS

Span: 44 ft. 6 in.
Length: 44 ft.
Height: 16 ft.
Weight: 18,650 lbs. loaded
Armament: None
Engines: Two Pratt & Whitney J–60s of 3,000 lbs. thrust each
Crew: Two plus seven passengers
Cost: $810,000

PERFORMANCE

Maximum speed: 538 mph.
Cruising speed: 500 mph.
Range: 1,700 miles
Service ceiling: 42,000 ft.

SPECIFICATIONS

Span: 23 ft. 6 in.
Length: 51 ft. 9 in.
Height: 15 ft. 9 in.
Weight: 18,080 lbs. max.
Armament: One NR–30 30mm cannon plus two K–13A air–to–air missiles
Engine: Tumansky R–11F–300 of 12,675 lbs. thrust w/afterburner.
Crew: One

PERFORMANCE
(estimated)
Maximum speed: 1,300 mph.
Cruising speed: 550 mph.
Range: 400 miles
Service ceiling: 50,000 ft.

MIKOYAN–GUREVICH MiG–21F "FISHBED"

The MiG–21F is a short–range day fighter–interceptor and the first major production version of the popular MiG–21 series. It is one of many versions of this aircraft that have served in the air arms of many nations around the world. The E–5 prototype of the MiG–21 was first flown in 1955 and made its first public appearance during the Soviet Aviation Day display at Moscow's Tushino Airport in June 1956. During the Vietnam War, MiG–21s were often used against U.S. aircraft. Between April 26, 1965, and January 8, 1973, USAF F–4s and B–52s downed 68 MiG–21s. More than 30 countries — including nations friendly to the U.S.—have flown the MiG–21. At least 15 versions of the MiG–21 have been produced, some outside the Soviet Union. Estimates place the number built at more than 8,000, a production total exceeding that of any other modern jet aircraft.

The MiG–21F on display appears to have been built in Czechoslovakia and to have flown in the air force of that nation. It is painted and marked as a MiG–21PF of the North Vietnamese Air Force during the Vietnam War. It was obtained by the Museum through an exchange with a private individual.

NORTHROP YF–5A "FREEDOM FIGHTER"

The F–5 is a supersonic fighter combining low cost, ease of maintenance, and great versatility. More than 2,000 F–5 aircraft have been procured by the USAF for use by allied nations. The F–5, which resembles the USAF Northrop T–38 trainer, is suitable for various types of ground–support and aerial intercept missions, including those which would have to be conducted from sod fields in combat areas.

The F–5 first flew on July 30, 1959 and deliveries to the Tactical Air Command for instructing foreign pilots began in April 1964. Pilots from Iran and South Korea were the first to be trained in the F–5, followed by pilots from Norway, Greece, Taiwan, Spain, and other Free World nations which have adopted the F–5. A two place combat trainer version, the F–5B, first flew in February 1964. In 1966–67, a USAF squadron of F–5s flew combat missions in Southeast Asia for operational evaluation purposes.

The aircraft on display at the Air Force Museum, one of three prototypes ordered, was delivered in 1970. It is painted as a "Skoshi Tiger" of the 4503rd Tactical Fighter Squadron, which combat tested the F-5 in Vietnam in 1965-67. The 4503rd TFS later was redesignated the 10th Fighter (Commando) Squadron in March 1966. In October 1966, the 10th F(C)S began training South Vietnamese Air Force (VNAF) pilots.

SPECIFICATIONS

Span: 25 ft. 10 in.
Length: 47 ft. 2 in.
Height: 13 ft. 2 in.
Weight: 20,576 lbs. loaded
Armament: Two 20mm cannons, rockets, missiles and 5,500 lbs. of bombs externally
Engines: Two General Electric J85s of 4,080 lbs. thrust each with afterburner
Cost: $752,000

PERFORMANCE

Maximum speed: 925 mph.
Cruising speed: 575 mph.
Maximum range: 1,100 miles
Service ceiling: 50,700 ft.

SPECIFICATIONS

Span: 50 ft. 1/4 in.
Length: 40 ft.
Height: 15 ft. 9 5/8 in.
Weight: 24,872 lbs. max.
Armament: Four 20 mm cannons and wide assortment of bombs, rockets, mines, grenades, flares and gun pods
Engine: Wright R–3350 of 2,700 hp.
Cost: $414,000

PERFORMANCE

Maximum speed: 325 mph.
Cruising speed: 240 mph.
Range: 1,500 miles
Service ceiling: 26,200 ft.

DOUGLAS A–1E "SKYRAIDER"

The history of the Skyraider began during WW II when Douglas submitted a design to the U.S. Navy for the XBT2D–1 as a replacement for the famous SBD dive–bomber. The result was a new airplane designated the "AD," which made its first flight on March 18, 1945. For the next 12 years there was constant improvement in the airplane up through the AD–7. 3,180 Skyraiders were delivered to the Navy, many of which were used during the Korean War.

In 1963, the U.S. Air Force began a program to modify the AD–5 Skyraider for service in Vietnam and redesignated it the A–1E. Because of its ability to carry large bomb loads, absorb heavy ground fire, and fly for long periods at low altitude, the A–1E was particularly suited for close–support missions.

The A–1E on display was the airplane flown by Major Bernard Fisher on March 10, 1966 when he rescued a fellow pilot shot down over South Vietnam in the midst of enemy troops, a deed for which he was awarded the Medal of Honor. The airplane, severely damaged in combat in South Vietnam, was returned in 1967 for preservation by the U.S. Air Force Museum.

BELL UH–1P "IROQUOIS"

The UH–l evolved from a 1955 Army competition for a new utility helicopter. The Army employed it in various roles including that of an armed escort or attack gunship in Vietnam. The USAF, USN, and USMC eventually adopted the model as did Canada, Brazil, and West Germany. The initial Army designation was HU–1, which led to the common unofficial nickname of "Huey." It was redesignated in 1962 as the UH–1 under a tri-service agreement.

USAF orders for the Huey began in 1963 for UH–1Fs, intended for support duties at missile sites, and for TH–1Fs for instrument and hoist training and medical evacuation. The HH–l H incorporated a longer fuselage and larger cabin for a crew of two and up to eleven passengers or six litters. The USAF ordered these in 1970 as local base rescue helicopters to replace the HH–43 "Huskie." The first of the USAF's UH–1Ns, a twin–engine utility version capable of cruising on one engine, was obtained in 1970.

The Huey on display served in South Vietnam in 1968–71 with the 20th Special Operations Squadron. In June 1969, its designation was changed from UH–1F to UH–1P, one of a few –Fs modified for a classified psychological warfare role. It was flown to the USAF Museum in April, 1980.

SPECIFICATIONS
Rotor diameter: 48 ft. 0 in.
Overall length: 57 ft. 0 in.
Height: 14 ft. 11 in.
Weight: 9,000 lbs. max.
Armament: None
Engine: General Electric T–58 of 1070 shaft hp.
Cost: $273,000
Crew: One or two

PERFORMANCE
(UH–1F)
Maximum speed: 140 mph.
Cruising speed: 115 mph.
Range: 330 miles
Service ceiling: 24,830 ft.

SPECIFICATIONS

Span: 55 ft. 7 in.
Length: 107 ft. 5 in.
Height: 18 ft. 6 in.
Weight: 170,000 lbs. loaded
Armament: None
Engines: Two Pratt & Whitney J58s of 32,500 lbs. thrust each with afterburner
Crew: Two

PERFORMANCE

Maximum speed: Plus 2,000 mph.
Range: Plus 2,900 miles
Service ceiling: Plus 85,000 ft.

LOCKHEED SR–71A

The SR–71, unofficially known as the "Blackbird," is a long–range, advanced, strategic reconnaissance aircraft developed from the Lockheed A–12 and YF–12A aircraft. The first flight of an SR–71 took place on December 22, 1964, and the first SR–71 to enter service was delivered to the 4200th (later, 9th) Strategic Reconnaissance Wing at Beale AFB, California, in January 1966. The U.S. Air Force retired its fleet of SR–71s on January 26, 1990, because of a decreasing defense budget and high costs of operation.

Throughout its nearly 24–year career, the SR–71 remained the world's fastest and highest–flying operational aircraft. From 80,000 feet it could survey 100,000 square miles of the Earth's surface per hour. On July 28, 1976, an SR–71 set two world records for its class: an absolute speed record of 2,193.167 miles per hour and an absolute altitude record of 85,068.997 feet.

On March 21, 1968, in the aircraft on display, Maj. (later General) Jerome F. O'Malley and Maj. Edward D. Payne made the first operational SR–71 sortie. During its career, this aircraft accumulated 2,981 flying hours and flew 942 total sorties (more than any other SR–71), including 257 operational missions, from Beale AFB, California; Palmdale, California; Kadena Air Base, Okinawa and RAF (Base) Mildenhall, England. The aircraft was flown to the Museum in March 1990.

DeHAVILLAND C–7A "CARIBOU"

The C–7A was a twin–engine, short takeoff and landing (STOL) utility transport built by DeHavilland Aircraft of Canada, Ltd. It was used primarily for tactical airlift missions in forward battle areas with short, unimproved airstrips. It could carry 26 fully equipped paratroops or up to 20 litter patients. As a cargo aircraft the Caribou could haul more than three tons of equipment.

The Caribou made its first flight in 1958. In 1959 the U.S. Army flew several prototypes for evaluation and, in 1961, the first 22 out of a total of 159 production versions were delivered to the Army. Originally designated AC–1, the aircraft was redesignated CV–2 in 1962 and retained that designation for the remainder of its Army career. In January 1967, when responsibility for all fixed–wing tactical transports was transferred to the U.S. Air Force, the Caribou received the designation C–7. During the Southeast Asian conflict, the Caribou's STOL capability made it particularly suitable for delivering troops, supplies, and equipment to isolated outposts.

The C–7A on display is a Southeast Asia combat veteran which later served with the Air Force Reserve. It was flown to the USAF Museum in May 1983.

SPECIFICATIONS

Span: 95 ft. 7 in.
Length: 72 ft. 7 in.
Height: 31 ft. 8 in.
Weight: 28,500 lbs. max.
Armament: None
Engines: Two Pratt & Whitney R–2000–7M2s of 1,450 hp. ea.
Crew: Three
Cost: $800,000

PERFORMANCE

Maximum speed: 216 mph.
Cruising speed: 152 mph.
Range: 1,175 miles
Service ceiling: 24,800 ft.

SPECIFICATIONS

Span: 34 ft. 11 in.
Length: 67 ft.
Height: 20 ft. 2 in.
Weight: 54,580 lbs. max.
Armament: One M61 20mm Vulcan cannon plus 14,000 lbs. of ordnance— conventional bombs, rocket packs, missiles and special weapons.
Engine: One 175–P–19W of 26,500 lbs. thrust.
Cost: $2,237,000.

PERFORMANCE

Maximum speed: 831 mph.
Cruise speed: 596 mph.
Range: 1,500 miles
Service ceiling: 50,000 ft.

REPUBLIC F–105G "THUNDERCHIEF"

The F–105 (affectionately nicknamed "Thud") evolved from a project begun in 1951 by Republic Aviation to develop a supersonic tactical fighter–bomber to replace the F–84F. The prototype first flew on October 22, 1955, but the first production aircraft, an F–105B, was not delivered to the USAF until 1958. The F–105D all–weather strike fighter and the two–place F–105F dual–purpose trainer–fighter also were built before F–105 production (833 aircraft) ended in 1964. No "C" or "E" series were produced, and the "G"s were modified from F–105Fs.

The "Thunderchief" on display began operational service in 1964 as a standard F–105F. In 1967 it joined the 355th Tactical Fighter Wing (TFW) in Thailand and for nearly three years flew combat missions over Vietnam where it became one of a select few claiming three MiG kills. In 1970 it was fitted with electronic counter–measure equipment and joined the 388th TFW for "Wild Weasel" duty, attacking enemy surface–to–air missile (SAM) sites. In 1972, the aircraft was modified to the improved F–105G "Wild Weasel" configuration. After another year in Thailand, it was assigned to the 35th TFW at George AFB, California. It remained there until February 1980 when it was flown to the USAF Museum. It is marked as it was when assigned to the 561st Tactical Fighter Squadron based at Korat RTAFB, Thailand in 1972–1973.

HELIO U–10D "SUPER COURIER"

The Super Courier is a light utility transport developed from a civilian design first tested in 1949. Its short takeoff and landing (STOL) capability allows it to operate from a clearing the size of a football field, and its ability to fly very slowly at speeds of approximately 25 to 35 mph makes it an excellent aircraft for visual reconnaissance.

The original version of the USAF Super Courier made its first flight in 1958. The USAF purchased three aircraft for evaluation the same year, designating them L–28As and later redesignating them U–10As. Eventually, more than 100 additional U–10s were ordered, mainly for use by air commando units in Southeast Asia. It was used for liaison, light cargo, small supply drop operations, psychological warfare (dropping leaflets and broadcasting propaganda), forward air controller, and reconnaissance missions.

The U–10D on display has been painted and marked as an aircraft assigned to the 5th Air Commando Squadron in Southeast Asia in 1968.

SPECIFICATIONS

Span: 39 ft.
Length: 30 ft. 8 in.
Height: 8 ft. 10 in.
Weight: 3,600 lbs. loaded
Armament: None
Engine: One Lycoming GO–480 six–cylinder engine of 295 hp.
Crew: One (plus five passengers)
Cost: $73,000

PERFORMANCE

Maximum speed: 180 mph.
Cruising speed: 160 mph.
Range: 1,100 miles
Service ceiling: 20,500 ft.

SPECIFICATIONS

Span: 67 ft. 6 in.
Length: 58 ft. 2 in.
Height: 25 ft. 8 in.
Weight: 41,500 lbs. max.
Armament: None
Engines: Four General Electric T64s of 3,080 hp. each

PERFORMANCE

Maximum speed: 400 mph.
Cruising speed: 235 mph.
Range: 820 miles
Service ceiling: 25,000 ft.

CHANCE–VOUGHT/LTV XC–142A

The tilt–wing XC–142A was an experimental aircraft designed to investigate the operational suitability of vertical/short takeoff and landing (V/STOL) transports. Such an aircraft would permit rapid movement of troops and supplies into unprepared areas under all–weather conditions. An XC–142A first flew conventionally on Sept. 29, 1964 and on Jan. 11, 1965, completed its first transitional flight by taking off vertically, changing to forward flight, and finally landing vertically.

Tilting the wing and engines skyward permitted vertical takeoff like a helicopter and then the wing and engines were gradually tilted forward to provide the greater speed of a fixed–wing aircraft in forward flight. The engines were linked together so that a single engine could turn all four propellers and the tail rotor. In tests the XC–142A was flown from airspeeds of 35 mph backwards to 400 mph forward. XC–142As were tested extensively by the Army, Navy, Air Force and NASA.

The aircraft on display, the only remaining XC–142A, was one of five built. It was flown to the Museum in 1970.

CESSNA O–1G "BIRD DOG"

The O–1G is a two–place observation and liaison aircraft developed from the commercial Cessna Model 170 in 1949. Originally designated as L–19s, "Bird Dogs" were used by the USAF, Army, and Marines for such tasks as artillery spotting, front–line communications, medical evacuation, and pilot training.

In Vietnam, O–1s were used by forward air controllers (FACs) for reconnaissance. A "FAC," often an experienced fighter pilot, was assigned to a specific geographical area, so that he could readily identify enemy activity. If a FAC observed enemy ground targets, he marked them with smoke rockets so they could be easily attacked by fighter–bombers. The FAC remained on the scene to report bombing results.

The USAF ordered more than 3,200 "Bird Dogs," most of which were built as L–19As between 1950 and 1959. The O–1G on display was transferred to the Museum in 1971.

SPECIFICATIONS

Span: 36 ft.
Length: 25 ft. 10 in.
Height: 9 ft. 2 in.
Weight: 2,400 lbs. loaded
Armament: Generally none except smoke rockets
Engine: Continental O–470 of 213 hp.
Cost: $11,000
Crew: Two

PERFORMANCE

Maximum speed: 150 mph.
Cruising speed: 115 mph.
Range: 530 miles
Service ceiling: 20,300 ft.

PRESIDENTIAL AIRCRAFT

DOUGLAS C–54C "SKYMASTER"

This aircraft, named the *Sacred Cow*, was built in 1944 for use by President Franklin D. Roosevelt. It is a Douglas C-54 transport aircraft with extensive interior modifications. One special feature is an elevator behind the passenger cabin to lift the president in his wheelchair in and out of the plane. The passenger compartment includes a conference room with a large desk and bullet-proof picture window. President Roosevelt made his first and only flight in this aircraft, traveling to Yalta in the USSR in February 1945 for a major international wartime conference with the leaders of Great Britain and the USSR. After Roosevelt's death in April 1945, President Truman signed the National Security Act of 1947 while on board the *Sacred Cow*. This act established the Air Force as an independent service, making the *Sacred Cow* the "birthplace" of the U.S. Air Force. In 1983 the Sacred Cow was shipped to the U.S. Air Force Museum. Restoration began in 1985. After ten years and more than 34,000 hours of work, the restoration was completed. The aircraft now appears as it did during President Roosevelt's trip to Yalta.

SPECIFICATIONS

Span: 117 ft. 6 in. **Length:** 93 ft. 5 in.
Height: 27 ft. 7 in. **Weight:** 80,000 lbs. loaded
Engines: Four Pratt & Whitney R-2000 Engines of 1,450 hp each
Crew: 7 (plus 15 passengers)

PERFORMANCE

Maximum speed: 300 mph
Cruising speed: 245 mph
Range: 3,900 statute miles
Service ceiling: 30,000 ft.

PRESIDENTIAL AIRCRAFT

DOUGLAS VC–118 "LIFTMASTER"

The VC–118 was a military variation of the Douglas DC–6 commercial airliner. In 1947, USAAF officials ordered the 29th production DC–6 to be modified as a replacement for the aging C–54C "Sacred Cow" Presidential aircraft. It differs from the standard DC–6 configuration in that the aft fuselage was converted into a stateroom; the main cabin seated 24 passengers or could be made up into 12 "sleeper" berths. The VC–118 was formally commissioned into the AAF on July 4, 1947, and was nicknamed *Independence* for the President's hometown in Missouri. Probably the plane's most historic flight occurred when it carried President Truman to Wake Island in October 1950 to discuss the Korean situation with Gen. Douglas MacArthur.

In May 1953, after nearly six years of White House service, the *Independence* was retired as a Presidential aircraft and subsequently served several Air Force organizations as a VIP transport. It was retired for display at the USAF Museum in 1965. In 1977-78, Museum personnel restored the Independence to its former presidential markings and eagle–like paint scheme.

SPECIFICATIONS

Span: 117 ft. 6 in.
Height: 28 ft. 5 in.
Length: 100 ft. 7 in.

Weight: 93,200 lbs. max.
Engines: Four Pratt & Whitney R–2800s of 2,400 hp. each (with water injection)

PERFORMANCE

Maximum speed: 360 mph.
Cruising speed: 320 mph.
Range: 4,400 miles
Service ceiling: 31,200 ft.

PRESIDENTIAL AIRCRAFT

LOCKHEED VC–121E "CONSTELLATION"

The C–121 is the military version of the famed "Constellation" commercial transport. During WW II, the AAF purchased 22 early model Constellations which were designated C–69s, and between 1948 and 1955 the USAF ordered 150 C–121s for use as cargo and passenger carriers, executive transports and airborne early warning picket ships.

The aircraft on display, the only VC–121E built, was President Eisenhower's personal airplane between 1954 and 1961. Mrs. Eisenhower christened it "Columbine III" in honor of the official flower of Colorado, her adopted home state, in ceremonies on November 24, 1954. "Columbine III" served as the Presidential aircraft until President Eisenhower left office in January 1961. It remained in service transporting government officials and visiting foreign dignitaries throughout the world until it was retired to the U.S. Air Force Museum in 1966.

SPECIFICATIONS

Span: 123 ft.
Height: 24 ft. 9 in.
Armament: None
Cost: $2,647,000

Length: 116 ft. 2 in.
Weight: 133,000 lbs. max.
Engines: Four Wright R–3350s of 3,400 hp. each

PERFORMANCE

Maximum speed: 330 mph.
Cruising speed: 255 mph.

PRESIDENTIAL AIRCRAFT

BELL UH–13J "SIOUX"

The UH–13J was the Air Force's version of the Bell commercial model 47J Ranger helicopter. Two UH–13Js were purchased in March 1957 for use as the first Presidential helicopters. On July 13, President Eisenhower became the first Chief Executive to fly in a helicopter when he took off from the White House lawn in the sister ship of the Sioux on display.

On March 1, 1962, following their assignment as Presidential aircraft, the two UH–13Js were reassigned to Bolling Air Force Base on the outskirts of Washington. For the next five years they were used to carry high–ranking Department of Defense personnel and numerous foreign dignitaries. In July 1967, they were retired from service, one going to the Smithsonian Institution and the other to the U.S. Air Force Museum.

SPECIFICATIONS

Main rotor diameter: 37 ft. 2 in.
Overall length: 43 ft. 4 in.
Weight: 2,800 lbs. loaded
Engine: Lycoming 0–435 of 240 hp.

Tail rotor diameter: 5 ft. 10 in.
Height: 9 ft. 4 in.
Armament: None
Cost: $65,000

PERFORMANCE

Maximum speed: 105 mph.
Cruising speed: 100 mph.
Range: 300 miles
Service ceiling: 17,000 ft.

AERO COMMANDER U-4B

The U-4B, an Air Force version of the L-26 Aero Commander, was used by President Dwight D. Eisenhower from 1956 to 1960 for short trips. It was the smallest "Air Force One," and the first presidential aircraft to have only two engines. The U-4B was also the first presidential aircraft to carry the familiar blue and white paint scheme. After President Eisenhower left office the aircraft was used for transporting high-ranking government officials. On October 1, 1969, it was transferred to the Air Force Academy where it was used for cadet parachute training and the Academy's skydiving team. In November 1977, the U-4B was sent to the Nebraska Civil Air Patrol. It was obtained by the Museum from a private owner in 1996 and placed on display in July 1997.

SPECIFICATIONS

Span: 44 ft. 1 in.
Height: 14 ft. 9.5in.
Engines: Lycoming GSO 480-AiA6 of 340 hp

Length: 35 ft. 5 in.
Weight: 4,300 lbs. (empty)
7,000 lbs. (loaded)

PERFORMANCE

Maximum speed: 260 mph.
Cruise speed: 230 mph.
Range: 1,500 statute miles
Service ceiling: 24,300 ft.

PRESIDENTIAL AIRCRAFT

VC-137C (BOEING 707) SAM 26000

This Boeing 707-320B was specially outfitted in 1962 to be the official aircraft of the President of the United States. The designation "Air Force One" was given to this Air Force aircraft only when the President was aboard, otherwise it was known by the tail number as SAM (Special Air Mission) 26000.

On October 10, 1962, the VC-137C, 26000, entered Air Force service directly from Boeing. President Kennedy had the aircraft painted in striking blue and white instead of the usual military colors to give the aircraft a distinctive look. The words "United States of America" were emblazoned on the fuselage and an American flag was painted on the tail. This aircraft was part of the presidential support fleet from 1962 to 1998.

This airplane flew President Kennedy to Dallas, Texas, on November 22, 1963, where he was assassinated, and it was on this airplane that Vice President Lyndon B. Johnson was sworn in as the 36th President of the United States.

SPECIFICATIONS

Span: 145 ft. 9in. **Length:** 152 ft. 11in.
Height: 42 ft. 5in. **Weight:** 258,000 lbs
Engine: Four Pratt & Whitney TF33 (JT3D-3) turbofans.
Crew: 7 or 8   **Load:** 40 passengers or 26,200 lbs of cargo.

PERFORMANCE

Maximum speed: 604 mph. **Ceiling:** Above 43,000 ft
Range: 6,000+ miles

PRESIDENTIAL AIRCRAFT

BEECH VC-6A

The VC–6A is a ten–place turboprop executive transport that was operated by the 89th Military Airlift Wing at Andrews AFB, Maryland, to transport visiting dignitaries and high–level government personnel. It is a standard Beechcraft King Air B90 with a "VIP" interior and is the only one of its type purchased by the Air Force. The aircraft's features include full pressurization for travel comfort at high altitudes, and all–weather navigation and de–icing equipment.

This aircraft was placed in service in early 1966. During the early part of its operational career, it was used to transport President Lyndon B. Johnson and members of his family between Bergstrom AFB, Texas, near Austin, and the Johnson family ranch near Johnson City. During this time, the aircraft became informally known as the "Lady Bird Special." After leaving presidential service, the VC–6A continued in its special executive transport role with the 89th Military Airlift Wing until it was retired to the USAF Museum on September 6, 1985.

SPECIFICATIONS

Span: 50 ft. 3 in. **Length:** 36 ft. 6 in.
Height: 14 ft. 8 in. **Weight:** 9,705 lbs. max.
Engines: Two Pratt & Whitney PT6A–20 turboprop of 550 hp. ea.
Crew: Two

PERFORMANCE

Maximum speed: 256 mph.
Range: 1,400 miles
Service ceiling: 32,900 ft.

PRESIDENTIAL AIRCRAFT

LOCKHEED VC–140B "JET STAR"

The C–140 is a military version of the Lockheed Model 1329 light jet transport. The prototype Jet Star was first flown on September 4, 1957, only 241 days after design completion. Production began in 1960. Although the majority of those produced were built for the civilian market, the U.S. Air Force bought 16 Jet Stars as C–140As and –Bs, the first of which was delivered in late 1961. Five C–140As were assigned to the Air Force Communications Command for use in evaluating military navigation aids and operations. Eleven C–140Bs were assigned to the Military Airlift Command for operational support airlift. Six of them were flown as VC–140Bs on special government and White House airlift missions by the 89th Military Airlift Wing at Andrews AFB, Maryland.

The VC–140B on display carried Presidents Nixon, Ford, Carter and Reagan a number of times, although it was not the primary presidential aircraft. Whenever the President was aboard, it flew under the radio call sign "Air Force One." This Jet Star ended its 26 years of service when it was flown to the USAF Museum on July 16, 1987.

SPECIFICATIONS

Span: 54 ft. 11 in.
Height: 20 ft. 5 in.
Engines: Four Pratt & Whitney J–60 turbojets of 3,000 lbs. thrust each
Crew: Four (plus eight passengers)

Length: 60 ft. 5 in.
Weight: 41,000 lbs. max.

PERFORMANCE

Maximum speed: 598 mph.
Cruising speed: 520 mph.
Range: 2,200 miles

DOUGLAS X–3 "STILETTO"

The twin–turbojet X–3, the only one built, was designed to test features of an aircraft suitable for sustained flights at supersonic speeds and high altitudes. A secondary mission was to investigate the use of new materials such as titanium and to explore new construction techniques.

The X–3 made its first test flight at Edwards AFB, California on October 20, 1952 and flew supersonically in June 1953. Unlike the X–1, X–2, and X–15 which were released in mid-air from a "mother plane," the X–3 operated in a more conventional manner by taking off from the ground. Engine development difficulties forced the use of lower powered engines than originally planned, prohibiting the X–3 from achieving its design potential. However, data gained from the X–3 program was of great benefit in the development of the F–104, X–15, SR–71 and other high performance aircraft. The X–3 was transferred to the U.S. Air Force Museum in 1956.

SPECIFICATIONS

Span: 22 ft. 8 in.　　**Length:** 66 ft. 10 in.
Height: 12 ft. 6 in.　　**Weight:** 22,400 lbs. max.
Engines: Two Westinghouse J34s of 3,370 lbs. thrust each
(4,900 lbs. thrust with afterburner)

PERFORMANCE

Maximum speed: Designed for Mach 2
Cruising speed: Not applicable
Range: Not applicable
Service ceiling: 38,000 ft.

X-PLANES

NORTHROP X-4

The X-4 was developed for the study of flight characteristics of swept wing, semi-tailless aircraft at transonic (about Mach .85) speeds. Northrop built two X-4s. The No. 1 aircraft was first flown by Northrop on December 16, 1948, and the second X-4 made its initial flight on June 7, 1949. The No. 1 aircraft was grounded after its 10th flight to provide spare parts for the No. 2 aircraft. Northrop's part of the test program ended on February 17, 1950, with the 20th flight of the remaining X-4. Although both aircraft were turned over to the Air Force and then to the National Advisory Committee for Aeronautics (NACA) in May 1950, only the No. 2 X-4 was used in the joint USAF/NACA program to explore stability problems near the speed of sound. The program ended in September 1953 with the 102nd and last flight of this, the No. 2 aircraft, after proving that swept wing aircraft without horizontal tails were not suitable for transonic flight. Both aircraft survived the test program without serious incident. The No. 1 X-4 is displayed at the Air Force Academy. The No. 2 aircraft was transferred to the Museum shortly after the program ended. It was restored by the Western Museum of Flight, Hawthorne, California.

SPECIFICATIONS

Span: 26 ft. 10 in. **Length:** 23 ft. 3 in.
Height: 14 ft. 10 in. **Weight:** 7,550 lbs. max.
Engine: Two Westinghouse XJ-30 turbojet engines of 1,600 lbs. thrust each

PERFORMANCE

Maximum speed: 640 mph.
Cruising speed: 480 mph.
Maximum endurance: 44 min.
Service ceiling: 44,000 ft.

BELL X–5

The X–5 was the world's first airplane to vary the sweepback of its wings in flight. It was built to prove the theory that by increasing the sweepback of an airplane's wings after takeoff, a higher maximum speed could be obtained, while still retaining a relatively low takeoff and landing speed and higher rate of climb with the wings swept forward. The X–5 was based upon the design of a Messerschmitt P. 1101 airplane discovered in Germany at the end of World War II, although the P. 1101 could vary its sweep only on the ground.

The first X–5 flight was made on June 20, 1951. On the airplane's ninth flight, its wings were operated through the full sweep range of 20° to 60°.

Two X–5s were built and flown. One crashed and was destroyed on October 13, 1953 when it failed to recover from a spin at 60° sweepback. The other was delivered to the U.S. Air Force Museum in March 1958.

SPECIFICATIONS
Span: with wings extended, 32 ft. 9 in.;
with wings swept, 22 ft. 8 in.
Length: 33 ft. 4 in.   **Height:** 12 ft.
Weight: 9,800 lbs. loaded
Engine: Allison J35 of 4,900 lbs. thrust

PERFORMANCE
Maximum speed: 690 mph.
Cruising speed: 600 mph.
Range: 500 miles
Service ceiling: 50,700 ft.

X-PLANES

REPUBLIC XF–84H "THUNDERSTREAK"

The XF-84H, a joint Air Force-Navy project based on the Republic F-84F, was originally designed to combine the speed of a jet with the long range, low fuel consumption and low landing speed of a propeller-driven aircraft. The XF-84H used an Allison XT40-A-1 turboprop engine in a modified F-84 fuselage. Additional changes included a T-type tail and a triangular fin on top of the fuselage to reduce the high torque produced by the propeller.

Between July 22, 1955, and October 9, 1956, two XF-84H prototypes made twelve test flights. Eleven of the twelve ended in emergency landings. Sounds produced by the aircraft's turboprop engine caused nausea and headaches among the ground crews, earning the XF-84H the unofficial nickname "Thunder screech." Though the XF-84H was the fastest single-engine propeller-driven aircraft ever built, it never approached supersonic speed. Due to poor performance and high maintenance requirements, the XF-84H never became operational.

The Museum obtained the aircraft from Kern County, California, in 1999.

SPECIFICATIONS

Span: 33 ft. 7 in.
Height: 15 ft.
Engine: One Allison XT40 -A-1 of 5,850 shaft hp.

Length: 43 ft. 5 in.
Weight: 27,000 lbs. max.

PERFORMANCE

Maximum speed: 520 mph.
Range: 2,000 miles
Service ceiling: above 40,000 ft.

X-PLANES

NORTH AMERICAN XB–70 "VALKYRIE"

The XB–70, one of the world's most exotic airplanes, was conceived for the Strategic Air Command in the 1950s as a high–altitude bomber that could fly three times the speed of sound (Mach 3). Because of fund limitations, only two were built, not as bombers, but as research aircraft for the advanced study of aerodynamics, propulsion, and other subjects related to large supersonic aircraft. The Valkyrie was built largely of stainless–steel honeycomb sandwich panels and titanium. It was designed to make use of a phenomenon called "compression lift," achieved when the shock wave generated by the airplane flying at supersonic speeds supports part of the airplane's weight. For improved stability at supersonic speeds, the Valkyrie could droop its wingtips as much as 65 degrees.

The No. 1 XB–70 made its initial flight on September 21, 1964, and first achieved Mach 3 flight on October 14, 1965. The No. 2 airplane first flew on July 17, 1965, but on June 8, 1966, it crashed following a mid–air collision. The No. 1 airplane continued in its research program until flown to the Museum on February 4, 1969.

SPECIFICATIONS

Span: 105 ft.   **Length:** 185 ft. 10 in. without boom; 192 ft. 2 in. with boom
Height: 30 ft. 9 in.   **Weight:** 534,700 lbs. loaded
Engines: Six General Electric YJ–93s of 30,000 lbs. thrust each w/afterburner.

PERFORMANCE

Maximum speed: 2,056 mph.(Mach 3.1) at 73,000 ft.
Cruising Speed: 2,000 mph. (Mach 3.0) at 72,000 ft.
Range: 4,288 miles   **Service Ceiling:** 77,350 ft.

X-PLANES

NORTH AMERICAN X–15A–2

The X–15, designed to provide data on material and human factors of high–speed, high–altitude flight, made the first manned probes into the lower edges of space. It was built for speeds of up to 4,000 mph and altitudes of 50 miles, but these goals were exceeded on numerous occasions. Several X-15 pilots earned "astronaut" rating by attaining altitudes above 50 miles. The X–15 flight program contributed significantly to the Mercury, Gemini, and Apollo projects.

The X–15 was carried aloft by a B–52 and was released at about 45,000 feet and 500 mph. Its rocket engine then fired for the first 80 to 120 seconds of flight. The remainder of the 10 to 11 minute flight was powerless and ended with a 200 mph glide landing on a dry lake bed.

The first powered X–15 flight was made on September 17, 1959, and 199 flights were made between 1959 and 1968 by the three X–15s which were built. The No.1 X–15 is at the National Air and Space Museum and the No. 3 X–15 was destroyed in a crash. The No. 2 aircraft was retired to the U.S. Air Force Museum in October 1969.

SPECIFICATIONS

Span: 22 ft. 5 in.
Height: 14 ft.
Length: 52 ft. 5 in.
Weight: 56,132 lbs.
Engine: Reaction Motors YLR–99 rocket engine of over 50,000 lbs. thrust

PERFORMANCE

Maximum speed: 4,520 mph. (unofficial record)
Range: Over 250 miles(flight path distance)
Maximum altitude: 354,200 ft. (unofficial record)

GRUMMAN X–29A

The X-29 was built to explore state-of-the-art technologies in aircraft design. The most easily identified of these, the forward-swept wing (FSW), was combined with advanced materials, a forward mounted elevator (canard) and an electrical flight control system.

Grumman began building the first of two X-29As in 1982. The program was administered by the U.S. Air Force and jointly funded by the Defense Advanced Research Projects Agency (DARPA), the Air Force and the National Aeronautics and Space Administration (NASA).

The first X-29A (S/N 82-003) — the one displayed here — made its initial flight on December 14, 1984 at Edwards AFB, California. On December 13, 1985, during its 26th flight, this aircraft became the world's first FSW aircraft to exceed the speed of sound in level flight. After successfully completing the test program, the first X-29A was retired to the USAF Museum in late 1994. The second X-29A made its first flight on May 23, 1989 and continued to perform test flights well into the 1990s.

SPECIFICATIONS

Span: 27 ft. 2 in.
Height: 14 ft. 3 in.
Length: 48 ft. 1 in.
Weight: 17,303 lbs. maximum
Engine: General Electric F404 turbofan engine of 16,000 lbs. thrust

PERFORMANCE

Maximum speed: 1,200 mph
Cruising speed: 460 mph
Max. endurance: 60 min.
Ceiling: 55,000 ft.

X-PLANES

"TACIT BLUE"

The Tacit Blue aircraft was built to test advances in stealth technology. The U.S. Air Force, the Defense Advanced Research Projects Agency, and the Northrop Corporation worked together from 1978 to 1985 to demonstrate that curved surfaces on an aircraft result in a low radar return signal from ground radar. With such a low radar return signal, the Tacit Blue demonstrated that such an aircraft could operate safely close to the forward edge of the battlefield area without fear of being discovered by enemy radar. It could continuously monitor enemy forces behind the battlefield and provide targeting information to a ground command center.

The aircraft made its first flight in February 1982, and by the conclusion of the program in 1985, had flown 135 times. It had a digital fly-by-wire flight control system to help stabilize the aircraft. Tacit Blue had a single flush inlet on the top of the fuselage to provide air to its two engines.

SPECIFICATIONS

Span: 48 ft. 2 in.
Height: 10 ft. 7 in.
Length: 55 ft. 10 in.
Weight: 30,000 lbs. max.
Engines: Two Garrett ATF 3-6 high-bypass turbofan engines
Crew: One
Cost: Approx. $165,000,000

PERFORMANCE

Speed: Sub-sonic
Designed Operational Speed: 287 mph
Operating Altitude: 25-30,000 ft.

SPECIFICATIONS

Span: 38 ft.
Length: 29 ft. 2 in.
Height: 9 ft. 5 in.
Weight: 4,900 lbs. loaded
Armament: Four wing pylons can carry rockets, flares, 7.62 mini–gun pods, or other light ordnance
Engines: Two Continental 10–360s of 210 hp. each
Crew: Two
Cost: $92,000

PERFORMANCE

Maximum speed: 199 mph.
Cruising speed: 144 mph.
Range: 1,060 miles
Service ceiling: 19,300 ft.

CESSNA O–2A "SKYMASTER"

The O–2 was a military version of the Cessna Model 337 Super Skymaster. Distinguished by twin tail booms and tandem–mounted engines, it featured a tractor–pusher propeller arrangement. Derived from the Cessna Model 336, the Model 337 went into production for the civilian market in 1965. In late 1966, the USAF selected a military variant, designated O–2, to supplement the O–1 Bird Dog forward air controller (FAC) aircraft then operating in Southeast Asia. Having twin engines enabled the O–2 to absorb more ground fire and still return safely, endearing it to its crews. The O–2 first flew in January 1967 and production deliveries began in March. Production ended in June 1970 after 532 O–2s had been built for the USAF.

Two series were produced: the O–2A and the O–2B. The O–2A was equipped with wing pylons to carry rockets, flares, and other light ordnance. In the Forward Air Controller (FAC) role the O–2A was used for identifying and marking enemy targets with smoke rockets, coordinating air strikes and reporting target damage. The O–2B was a psychological warfare aircraft equipped with loudspeakers and leaflet dispensers. It carried no ordnance.

The O–2A on display was assigned to the 20th Tactical Air Support Squadron at Da Nang, South Vietnam in the late 1960s. It was transferred to the Museum in December 1982.

NORTH AMERICAN T–28B "TROJAN"

North American designed the T-28 to replace the World War II era T-6 trainer. First flown in 1949, the Trojan entered production in 1950. An 800 horsepower engine powered the U.S. Air Force version (T-28A) while the later U.S. Navy versions (T-28B and T-28C) were powered by a 1,425 hp engine. When production ended in 1957, North American had built a total of 1,948 of these three versions.

In 1962, the USAF began a program to modify more than 200 T–28s as tactical fighter–bombers for counterinsurgency warfare in Southeast Asia. Equipped with 1,425–hp. engines, these airplanes (redesignated the T–28D "Nomad") proved to be an effective weapon in close support missions against enemy ground troops. The South Vietnamese Air Force (VNAF) operated a number of USAF-supplied T-28Bs until the T-28Ds became available.

The T–28B on display was flown to the Museum in March, 1987, and is painted as a VNAF T-28B assigned to Bien Hoa Air Base in 1962.

SPECIFICATIONS
Span: 40 ft. 1 in.
Length: 33 ft.
Height: 12 ft. 8 in.
Weight: 8500 lbs. (max take-off load)
Armament: Two .50–cal. machine guns in detachable pods under wing, two l00–lb. bombs, or six 2.25 in. rockets
Engine: Wright R–1820 of 1,425 hp.

PERFORMANCE
Maximum speed: 346 mph..
Range: 1,060 miles
Service ceiling: 37,000 ft.

SPECIFICATIONS

Span: 126 ft. 2 in.
Length: 116 ft. 2 in.
Height: 27 ft.
Weight: 145,000 lbs.
Armament: None
Engines: Four Wright
R–3350s of 3,400 hp. ea.
Cost: $2,031,000

PERFORMANCE

Maximum speed: 290 mph.
Cruising speed: 240 mph.
Range: 4,000 miles
Service ceiling: 18,000 ft.

LOCKHEED EC–121D "CONSTELLATION"

The EC–121, originally designated as the RC–121, is a radar–picket modification of the USAF C–121 passenger airplane which evolved from the Lockheed "Constellation" commercial transport. The massive radomes above and below the fuselage carry six tons of electronic gear. These aircraft entered service with the Air Defense Command in 1953, flying patrols off the U.S. coasts as an aerial extension of the Distant Early Warning (DEW) Line. The Air Force ordered 82 RC–121s between 1951 and 1955, 72 of which were –Ds.

In Southeast Asia, these unarmed radar aircraft aided in downing enemy planes, directed U.S. aircraft to their aerial refueling tankers, and guided rescue planes to downed pilots.

The aircraft on display was nicknamed "Triple Nickel" because of its serial number (53–555). On Oct. 24, 1967 over the Gulf of Tonkin, it guided a U.S. fighter by radar into position to destroy an enemy MiG–21. This was the first time a weapons controller aboard an airborne radar aircraft had ever directed a successful attack on an enemy plane. "Triple Nickel" was retired to the Museum in 1971.

HAWKER SIDDELEY XV-6A "KESTREL"

The British-built Kestrel was designed with V/STOL (vertical/short takeoff and landing) capabilities, making it possible for it to operate from grass or semi-prepared surfaces. These qualities offered great operational flexibility. Four adjustable exhaust nozzles beneath the wing roots could be rotated to provide thrust for vertical, backward, or hovering flight as well as conventional forward movement.

The first Kestrel began conventional flight trials on March 13, 1961 in Britain. In 1962, the governments of the U.S., Britain, and the Federal Republic of Germany ordered nine aircraft for combined testing. They formed an evaluation squadron which conducted Kestrel trials between April and September 1965. Six of these trial aircraft were delivered later to the U.S. where, as XV-6As, they underwent additional testing of V/STOL fighter techniques. An improved version, known as the "Harrier," became the world's first operational V/STOL fighter when it entered Royal Air Force service in 1969.

When the aircraft on display was delivered to the museum in 1970 from Edwards AFB, it became the first airplane to be airlifted by the giant C-5A.

SPECIFICATIONS
Span: 22 ft. 11in.
Length: 42 ft. 6 in.
Height: 10 ft. 9 in.
Weight: 15,500 lbs. maximum
Armament: None
Engine: Bristol Siddeley Pegasus 5 of 15,200 lbs. thrust

PERFORMANCE
Maximum speed: 650 mph.
Cruising speed: 625 mph.

SPECIFICATIONS

Span: 38 ft. 5 in.
Length: 62 ft. 10 in.
Height: 16 ft. 6 in.
Armament: None. Some later equipped with 4 Sidewinder missiles.
Engines: Two General Electric J-79-GE-15s of 17,000 lbs. thrust each with afterburner
Crew: two
Cost: $2,260,000

PERFORMANCE

Maximum speed: 1,384 mph/ 1,204 knots.
Cruising speed: 575 mph 500 knots.
Max. Range: 1,632 statute miles/ 1,418 nautical miles without aerial refueling.
Service ceiling: 55,200 ft.

McDONNELL DOUGLAS RF-4C "PHANTOM II"

In the early 1960s, the USAF recognized the need for more tactical reconnaissance aircraft to reinforce the RF-101s then in service. The Air Force chose a modification of the F-4C fighter. The RF-4C development program began in 1962, and the first production aircraft made its initial flight on May 18, 1964. A total of 499 RF-4Cs were eventually accepted by the Air Force.

The RF-4C can carry a variety of cameras in three different stations in its nose section. It can take photos at both high and low altitude, day or night. The RF-4C carries no offensive armament, although during the last few years of its service some were fitted with four AIM-9 Sidewinder missiles for defense.

The first unit to fly the RF-4C operationally was the 16th Tactical Reconnaissance Squadron. In October 1965 that unit deployed to Southeast Asia to provide photographic reconnaissance of the growing conflict in South Vietnam. Since then RF-4Cs have been involved in reconnaissance missions around the world, including the Desert Shield/ Desert Storm operation in Iraq in 1990-1991.

The RF-4C on display was delivered to the USAF on September 9, 1965. It served in Vietnam, Japan, Korea, Europe, Cuba, and the Middle East. During Desert Shield/ Desert Storm, this aircraft flew a total of 172 missions, more than any other F-4 aircraft. When flown to the USAF Museum in May 1994, it had more than 7,300 hours of flying time.

165

CESSNA YA–37A

The YA–37A was modified from the standard T–37B primary trainer to evaluate the design as a counter–insurgency (COIN) attack/reconnaissance aircraft. First flown in September 1963, the airplane underwent performance and systems evaluation testing during 1964 at Edwards AFB, California, and Eglin AFB, Florida

Much valuable information was obtained from these tests with regard to future design requirements for COIN aircraft. One of the aircraft's remarkable features was its ability to carry out a mission with only one engine still operating.

The aircraft on display, one of two YAT–37Ds, was retired to the U.S. Air Force Museum in December 1964. However, it was recalled to active service in August 1966 for final design testing of the A–37 attack aircraft, urgently needed for close air support of ground forces in Southeast Asia.

This aircraft was retired to the Museum for a second time in July 1970 as the YA–37A.

SPECIFICATIONS
Span: 35 ft. 10 in.
Length: 29 ft. 4 in.
Height: 8 ft. 2 in.
Weight: 11,700 lbs. max.
Armament: Max. of 3,000 lbs. including one GAU–2/A 7.62mm "Gatling" gun, plus additional gun pods, high–explosive bombs, fire bombs, rockets, grenades, and/or missiles
Engines: Two General Electric J85s of 2,400 lbs. thrust each
Cost: $161,000

PERFORMANCE
Maximum speed: 535 mph.
Cruising speed: 410 mph.
Range: 1,200 miles
Service ceiling: 25,000 ft.

SPECIFICATIONS

Span: 40 ft.
Length: 41 ft. 7 in.
Height: 15 ft. 1 in.
Weight: 14,444 lbs. max.
Armament: Four M60C 7.62mm machine guns in fuselage sponsons, plus 3,600 lbs. of mixed ordnance or gun pods carried externally
Engines: Two Garrett–AiResearch T76s (–G–10, left; –G–12, right) of 715 shaft hp. each
Crew: Two
Cost: $480,000

PERFORMANCE

Maximum speed: 281 mph.
Cruising speed: 223 mph.
Range: 1,240 miles
Service ceiling: 26,000 ft.

NORTH AMERICAN ROCKWELL OV–10A "BRONCO"

The OV–10A was a twin–turboprop short takeoff and landing aircraft conceived by the Marine Corps and developed under an Air Force, Navy, and Marine Corps tri–service program. The first production OV–10A was ordered in 1966 and its initial flight took place in August 1967.

The Bronco's mission capabilities included observation, forward air control, helicopter escort, armed reconnaissance, gunfire spotting, utility and limited ground attack; however, the USAF acquired the Bronco primarily as a forward air control aircraft. Adding to its versatility is a rear fuselage compartment with a capacity of 3,200 pounds of cargo, five combat–equipped troops, or two litter patients and a medical attendant.

The first USAF OV–10As destined for combat arrived in Vietnam on July 31, 1968. A total of 157 OV–10As were delivered to the USAF before production ended in April 1969.

The aircraft on display was flown to the Museum on October 2, 1991, and is painted as it was when it served in Southeast Asia.

LOCKHEED AC–130A "SPECTRE" *AZRAEL*

The crew of this AC-130A gunship named "Azrael - Angel of Death" (Azrael in Jewish legends was a demon or evil spirit; a fallen angel) displayed courage and heroism during the closing hours of Desert Storm. On 26 February 1991, the allied ground forces were driving the Iraqi army out of Kuwait. The crew of Azrael, Spectre #54-1630, was sent to the Al Jahra highway between Kuwait City and Basrah, Iraq, to intercept the convoys of tanks, trucks, buses, and cars that were fleeing the battle. Facing numerous enemy batteries of SA-6 and SA-8 missiles and 37mm and 57mm radar guided anti-aircraft artillery, the crew attacked the enemy skillfully, inflicting significant damage to the convoys.

During the 1950s the C-130 "Hercules" was originally designed as an assault transport, but it was adapted for a variety of missions. The C-130 could transport up to 92 combat troops and their gear or 45,000 pounds of cargo. Where facilities were inadequate, the Hercules could deliver its cargo by parachute or by low altitude extraction without landing. The AC-130A Spectre is a C-130 that was converted to a side-firing gunship, primarily for night attacks against ground troops. The AC-130A was equipped with two 40mm cannons, two 20mm Vulcan cannons, and two 7.62mm miniguns. The Air Force Museum's AC-130A was retired in October 1995.

SPECIFICATIONS

Span: 132 ft. 7 in.
Length: 96 ft. 10 in.
Height: 38 ft. 6 in.
Weight: 124,200 lbs. max.
Armament: Two 7.62mm mini–guns, two 20mm and two 40mm cannons
Engines: Four Allison T–56–A–9D turboprops of 3,750 horsepower

PERFORMANCE

Maximum speed: 380 mph.
Cruising speed: 335 mph.
Range: 2,500 miles
Service ceiling: 33,000 ft.

SPECIFICATIONS

Span: 38 ft. 8 in.
Length: 46 ft. 1 in.
Height: 16 ft. 1 in.
Weight: 39,325 loaded
Armament: One M61A1 20mm rapid–fire cannon plus 15,000 lbs. of mixed ordnance.
Engine: One Allison TF41 turbofan engine of 14,250 lbs. thrust
Crew: One
Cost: $2,860,000

PERFORMANCE

Maximum speed: 663 mph.
Cruising speed: 545 mph.
Range: 3,044 miles
Service ceiling: 33,500 ft.

LTV A–7D "CORSAIR II"

The A–7D was a single–seat, tactical close air support aircraft. Although designed primarily as a ground attack aircraft, it also had limited air–to–air combat capability. It was derived from the basic A–7 originally developed by LTV for the U.S. Navy. The first USAF A–7D made its initial flight on April 5, 1968, and deliveries of production models began on December 23, 1968. When A–7D production ended in 1976, 459 had been delivered to the USAF. In 1973, the USAF began assigning A–7Ds to the Air National Guard (ANG), and by 1987 they were being flown by ANG units in ten states and Puerto Rico. The A–7D demonstrated its outstanding capability to attack ground targets while flown by the 354th Tactical Fighter Wing at Korat RTAFB, Thailand, during the closing months of the war in Southeast Asia. The Corsair II achieved its excellent accuracy with the aid of an automatic electronic navigation and weapon–delivery system.

The A–7D on display was flown on November 18, 1972, by Major Colin A. Clarke on a nine–hour rescue support mission in Southeast Asia for which he was awarded the Air Force Cross, the Air Force's second highest award for valor in combat. It was delivered to the USAF Museum on January 31, 1992.

SIKORSKY CH–3E

The CH–3E is the USAF version of the Sikorsky S–61 amphibious transport helicopter developed for the U.S. Navy. The USAF initially operated six Navy HSS–2 (SH–3A) versions of the S–61 in 1962, eventually designating them CH–3A/Bs. They were so successful the USAF ordered 75, modified as CH–3Cs, featuring a new rear fuselage design with a ramp for vehicles and other cargo. The first CH–3C was flown on June 17, 1963. When 41 CH–3Cs were updated with more powerful engines in 1966, they were redesignated as CH–3Es. Forty-five more were newly manufactured. Later, 50 CH–3Es were modified for combat rescue missions with armor, defensive armament, self–sealing fuel tanks, a rescue hoist, and in–flight refueling capability. They were redesignated HH–3Es and used extensively in Vietnam under the nickname "Jolly Green Giant."

The CH–3E on display—known as Black Mariah—is a veteran of the Southeast Asia war. In 1965 it was attached to the 20th Helicopter Squadron. Painted flat black (hence the nickname), it was used for highly classified special missions.

SPECIFICATIONS

Rotor diameter: 62 ft.
Length: 73 ft.
Height: 18 ft. 1 in.
Weight: 22,050 lbs. loaded
Armament: Provisions for two .50–cal. guns
Engines: Two General Electric T58–GE–5 turboshaft engines of 1,500 hp. each
Crew: Three
Cost: $796,000

PERFORMANCE

Maximum speed: 177 mph.
Cruising speed: 154 mph.
Range: 779 miles with external fuel tanks
Service ceiling: 21,000 ft.

SPECIFICATIONS

Span: 32 ft. swept;
63 ft. extended
Length: 73 ft. 6 in.
Height: 17 ft.
Weight: +100,000 lbs. max.
Armament: One 20mm M61A1
Vulcan cannon, plus a mix of 24
conventional or nuclear weapons
Engines: Two Pratt & Whitney
TF30–P–100 of 25,000 lbs. thrust
each with afterburner
Crew: Two
Cost: $8.2 million

PERFORMANCE

Maximum speed: 1,452 mph.
Cruising speed: 685 mph.
Range: 3,632 miles
Service ceiling: 57,000 ft.

GENERAL DYNAMICS F–111F "AARDVARK"

The versatile "swing wing" F-111 entered the USAF inventory in 1967. The F-111's wings are straight for takeoffs, landings, or slow speed flight, but by sweeping its wings rearward, it can exceed twice the speed of sound (Mach 2). In 1960 the Department of Defense combined the USAF's requirement for a fighter-bomber with a Navy need for an air superiority fighter, though the Navy eventually cancelled its program. In all, 566 F-111s of all series were built; 106 of them were production F-111Fs.

The F-111 was a long-range, all-weather strike aircraft capable of navigating at low level to reach targets deep in enemy territory and to deliver ordnance on the target. Primarily a bomber, the F-111 featured a sweep wing varying between 16 and 72.5 degrees, with side-by-side seating for a pilot and weapons system officer. The F-111F model was equipped with all-weather AN/AVQ-26 Pave Tack infra-red targeting designator/reader carried a pod-mounted turret. It could track and designate ground targets for laser, infra-red and electro-optical bombs.

This aircraft is painted and marked as it was when it served with the 48th Tactical Fighter Wing during Operation Desert Storm. It was flown to the Museum in July 1996.

MIKOYAN–GUREVICH MiG-23MLD (FLOGGER K)

The MiG-23/27 "Flogger" series of aircraft has been used extensively by the former Soviet Union and its Warsaw Pact allies. The MiG-23 series served as fighter-interceptors, with a secondary capability of ground attack. The MiG-23BN and MiG-27 were fighter-bomber variations. More than 4,000 MiG-23/27s are estimated to have been built.

The MiG-23 was designed in 1964-66 as a successor to the MiG-21. In addition to a much more powerful engine, the MiG-23's most significant new feature was its variable sweep wing. Like the USAF's swing wing F-111, the sweep of the wings could be changed in flight.

The MiG-23MLD Flogger K version was a modification of the MiG-23ML Flogger G and incorporated improved avionics, armament, and aerodynamic features. This -K is painted as one assigned to a Soviet Frontal Aviation Regiment, the tactical arm of the Soviet air force. It first was sold legally as a display aircraft by a Russian general to a Finnish company, supposedly to obtain funds to feed his troops. An American in Florida purchased it, but the Bureau of Alcohol, Tobacco and Firearms seized it when he imported it illegally without proper permits. The Museum acquired it from the National Air Intelligence Center in 1998.

SPECIFICATIONS

Span: 45 ft. 10 in. with wings spread;
25 ft. 6 in. with wings swept.
Length: 54 ft. 10 in.
Height: 15 ft. 10 in.
Weight: 39,250 lbs. max.
Armament: One twin-barrel 23mm cannon and various combinations of missiles, rockets and bombs
Engine: One Tumansky R-35F-300 with 28,660 lbs of thrust with afterburner.
Crew: One

PERFORMANCE

Maximum speed: 1,390 mph.
Cruising speed: 778 mph.
Range: 2206 miles
Service ceiling: 51,000 ft.
Combat radius: 715 statute miles

SPECIFICATIONS

(Data for KC-135A)
Span: 130 ft. 10 in.
Length: 136 ft. 3 in.
Height: 41 ft. 8 in.
Weight: 300,000 lbs. loaded
Armament: None
Engine: Four Pratt & Whitney J-57 turbojet engines of 13,750 lbs. thrust each with water injection
Crew: Four (plus 80 troops)
Cost: $3,398,000

PERFORMANCE

Maximum speed: 606 mph.
Cruising speed: 512 mph.
Range: 8,673 miles
Service ceiling: 50,000 ft.

BOEING NKC-135A "STRATOTANKER"

While the KC-135A is usually used for in-flight refueling, the NKC-135A Airborne Laser Lab is a modified version used for flight testing. Similar to the commercial Boeing 707, the slightly smaller KC-135 was designed to military specifications and operated at higher gross weights. The initial flight of a KC-135A took place on August 31, 1956, and the USAF accepted its first one on January 31, 1957. By 1966, 732 KC-135As had been built and the aircraft had become the USAF's standard tanker. It also was used for transporting cargo or personnel and by 1970 was serving in other roles too, including reconnaissance, electronic intelligence gathering, and project testing.

The NKC-135A on display is one of 14 KC-135As permanently converted for special testing. It was extensively modified by the Air Force Weapons Laboratory at Kirtland AFB, New Mexico, and used in an 11-year experiment to prove a high-energy laser could be operated in an aircraft and employed against airborne targets. During the experiment, the Airborne Laser Lab destroyed five AIM-9 Sidewinder air-to-air missiles and a Navy BQM-34A target drone.

The aircraft was flown to the Museum in May 1988.

FAIRCHILD REPUBLIC A–10A
"THUNDERBOLT II"

The A–10 is the first USAF aircraft designed specifically for close air support of ground forces. It is named for the famous P–47 Thunderbolt, a fighter often used in a close air support role during the latter part of WW II. The A–10 is designed for maneuverability at low speeds and low altitudes for accurate weapons delivery, and carries systems and armor to permit it to survive in this environment. It is intended for use against all ground targets, but specifically tanks and other armored vehicles. The Thunderbolt II's great endurance gives it a large combat radius and/or long loiter time in a battle area. Its short takeoff and landing capability permits operation from airstrips close to the front lines. Service at forward area bases with limited facilities is possible because of the A–10's simplicity of design.

The first prototype Thunderbolt II made its initial flight on May 10, 1972. A–10A production commenced in 1975. Delivery of aircraft to USAF units began in 1976 and ended in 1984.

The A–10A on display was flown on Jan. 21, 1991, by Captain Paul Johnson on an eight–hour rescue support mission during Operation Desert Storm for which he was awarded the Air Force Cross, the Air Force's second highest award for valor. It was delivered to the USAF Museum on Jan. 24, 1992.

SPECIFICATIONS

Span: 57 ft. 6 in.
Length: 53 ft. 4 in.
Height: 17 ft. 8 in.
Weight: 47,000 lbs.
Armament: One GAU–8/A 30mm Gatling gun and 16,000 lbs. of mixed ordnance
Engines: Two General Electric TF34–GE–100 turbofans of 9,000 lbs. thrust each
Crew: One
Cost: $2,400,000

PERFORMANCE

Maximum speed: 450 mph.
Cruising speed: 335 mph.
Range: 2,900 miles
Service ceiling: 44,200 ft.

SPECIFICATIONS

Span: 43 ft. 4 in.
Length: 65 ft. 11 in.
Height: 12 ft. 5 in.
Weight: 52,500 lbs. max.
Armament: Up to 4,000 lbs. of internal stores
Engines: Two GE F404–F1D2 engines of 10,600 lbs. thrust ea.
Crew: One
Cost: $42,600,000

PERFORMANCE

Maximum speed: High subsonic
Cruising speed: 684 mph./ 594 knots
Range: Unlimited with aerial refueling
Service ceiling: 45,000 ft.

LOCKHEED F–117A

The Lockheed F–117A was developed in response to an Air Force request for an aircraft capable of attacking high value targets without being detected by hostile radar systems. By the 1970s special materials and techniques had become available to aircraft designers that would allow them to design an aircraft with radar–evading or "stealth" qualities. The result was the F–117A, the world's first operational aircraft that fully incorporated radar–evading techniques.

The first F–117A flew on June 18, 1981 and the first F–117A unit, the 4450th Tactical Group, achieved initial operating capability in October 1983. The 4450th was renamed the 37th Tactical Fighter Wing in October 1989. The F–117A was first used in combat during Operation Just Cause on December 19, 1989 when two F–117As from the 37th TFW attacked military targets in Panama. The F–117A was again called into action during Operation Desert Shield/Storm in 1990–91 when the 415th and the 416th squadrons of the 37th TFW moved to a base in Saudi Arabia. During Operation Desert Storm the F–117As flew 1,271 sorties, achieving an 80 percent mission success rate while suffering no losses or battle damage. A total of 59 F–117As were built between 1981 and 1990. The F–117A was awarded the 1989 Collier Trophy, one of the most prized aeronautical awards in the world.

The aircraft on display is the second F–117A built and was specially modified and instrumented to test various systems. After its test program was completed the Air Force decided to retire the aircraft in 1991. It was then turned over to the USAF Museum and is marked as it appeared during tests conducted for the Air Force Systems Command between 1981 and 1991.

BOEING EC-135E "ARIA"

During the early 1960s, NASA and the Department of Defense(DoD) needed a very mobile tracking and telemetry platform to support the Apollo space program and other unmanned space flight operations. In a joint project, NASA and DoD contracted with McDonnell-Douglas and Bendix Corporation to modify eight Boeing C-135 Stratolifter cargo aircraft into Apollo/Range Instrumentation Aircraft (A/RIA). Equipped with a steerable seven foot antenna dish in its distinctive "Droop Snoot" or "Snoopy Nose", the EC-135N became operational in January 1968. The Air Force Eastern Test Range at Patrick AFB in Florida operated the A/RIAs until the end of the Apollo program in 1972 when the USAF renamed them Advanced Range Instrumentation Aircraft (ARIA)

Transferred to the 4950th Test Wing at Wright-Patterson AFB, Ohio in December, 1975, the ARIA fleet underwent numerous conversions including re-engining that changed the EC-135N to an EC-135E. By the 1990s, taskings for the ARIA dwindled because of high costs and improved satellite technology and the USAF transferred the aircraft to other programs such as J-STARS (Joint Surveillance and Target Attack Radar System).

The display aircraft was retired and flown to the Museum in November, 2000.

SPECIFICATIONS
Span: 130 ft. 10 in.
Length: 136 ft. 3 in.
Height: 38 ft. 4 in.
Weight: 275,500 lbs. (max take-off load)
Armament: None
Engine: Four Pratt & Whitney TF-33 turbo fan engines of 18,000 lbs. thrust
Crew: 11

PERFORMANCE
Maximum speed: 606 mph.
Cruising speed: 512 mph.
Service ceiling: 50,000 ft.

SPECIFICATIONS

Span: 43 ft.
Length: 64 ft. 2 in.
Height: 17 ft. 9 in.
Armament: One M61A2 20mm multi-barrel cannon; internal stations can carry AIM-9 infrared air-to-air missiles or 1,000 pound Joint Direct Attack Munitions
Engines: Two Pratt & Whitney YF-119-PW-100s

PERFORMANCE

Maximum speed: Mach 2+
Service ceiling: Above 50,000 ft.

LOCKHEED–BOEING–GENERAL DYNAMICS
YF-22

In 1981, the Air Force developed a requirement for an Advanced Tactical Fighter (ATF) as a new air superiority fighter. It would take advantage of the new technologies in fighter design on the horizon, including composite materials, lightweight alloys, advanced flight control systems, higher power propulsion systems, and stealth technology. Air Force leaders believed that these new technologies would make aircraft like the F-15 and F-16 obsolete early in the 21st Century. In 1985 the Air Force sent out formal requests for proposals to two aircraft manufacturing teams one led by Lockheed and the other by Northrop, to build the prototypes. The Lockheed and Northrop teams each built two prototypes, one with General Electric YF120 engines and one with Pratt & Whitney YF119 engines. Lockheed's aircraft were designated YF-22s and Northrop's were designated YF-23s. After extensive flight tests, the Lockheed-Boeing-General Dynamics team won the airframe competition and Pratt & Whitney the engine contract. In 1997 the AF sent the YF-22 prototype that had been equipped with the GE engines to the Air Force Museum. After it was refurbished and equipped with two Pratt & Whitney YF-119-PW-100 engines, it was placed on display in 1998.

NORTHROP B-2 "SPIRIT"

By the 1980s, the global spread of sophisticated air defense systems threatened the US Air Force's ability to destroy an enemy's most valued targets. To overcome this threat, the USAF adopted the revolutionary low-observable, or "stealth" technology first seen in the F-117A. To produce a long-range bomber capable of delivering large payloads of conventional or nuclear weapons, Northrop-Grumman merged the high aerodynamic efficiency of the "flying wing" design with stealth technologies to produce the B-2 Spirit. Constructed with composite materials, special coatings, and classified stealth technologies, the B-2 is virtually invisible to even the most sophisticated air defense radar systems.

The public first saw the highly classified B-2 on November 22, 1988, when it rolled out of its hangar at Air Force Plant 42 at Palmdale, California. The first B-2 flew on July 17, 1989, at Edwards AFB, California and Northrop-Grumman delivered the first operational B-2 on December 17, 1993.

With a crew of only two, the pilot in the left seat and the mission commander in the right, a typical combat mission consisted of a non-stop flight from its home base at Whiteman AFB, Missouri, to the target and back. During these missions, normally lasting more than 30 hours and requiring numerous aerial refuelings, each B-2 delivered up to 40,000 pounds of precision weapons.

The B-2 at the U.S. Air Force Museum is a ground static test prototype which has never flown. After completing its series of tests, it was turned over to the Museum for restoration and display.

(Photo: USAF)

SPECIFICATIONS

Wingspan: 172 ft.
Height: 17 ft.
Takeoff Weight: 336,500 lbs.
Engines: Four General Electric
      F-118-GE-100
      Turbofans

PERFORMANCE
Speed: High subsonic

GENERAL ATOMICS RQ-1 PREDATOR

The RQ-1 Predator is not just an aircraft but an entire unmanned aerial surveillance system. It provides military commanders with an intelligence, surveillance, and reconnaissance platform capable of flying over dangerous areas for extended periods without risk to a human pilot.

In flight, the Predator and its on-board sensors are controlled by the ground crew via a direct data link or when flown beyond the direct link, by a satellite data link. Using satellite data links, the information gathered by a Predator can be shared instantaneously with commanders around the world.

RQ-1 SPECIFICATIONS
Span: 48.7 ft.
Length: 27 ft.
Height: 6.9 ft.
Weight: 950 lbs. empty
Engines: One Rotax 912 of 81 hp.

PERFORMANCE
Cruising speed: 87 mph.

NORTHROP-GRUMMAN RQ-4A GLOBAL HAWK

RQ-4A SPECIFICATIONS
Span: 116 ft.
Length: 44 ft.

PERFORMANCE
Maximum speed: 400 mph.
Range: 13,000 + miles
Ceiling: 65,000+ ft.

Global Hawk is a high-altitude, long-endurance Unmanned Aerial Vehicle(UAV) that sends near real-time reconnaissance imagery to air, ground, and sea forces. Global Hawk's sophisticated electronics let it "see" through clouds and in the dark. Its "Synthetic-Aperture Radar/Moving Target Indicator" tracks small moving objects on the ground, and a powerful digital camera and infrared sensor let the RQ-4A gather imagery in any weather conditions, day or night. Satellites can relay Global Hawk imagery to military forces around the world.

In 2000, the Global Hawk set a record for jet-powered UAVs by flying more than 31.5 hours at a mean altitude of 65,100 feet.

The Advanced Cruise Missile is an air-to-ground cruise missile developed to provide the Air Combat Command (formerly Strategic Air Command) with a long range, highly survivable, strategic standoff weapon. The ACM uses laser sensor updates to give it high navigation accuracy and "stealth" technology to give it a low radar cross section enabling it to penetrate enemy defenses.

Up to 12 ACMs can be carried by a B-52H bomber allowing the bomber to attack multiple targets without penetrating enemy airspace. Full scale development of the ACM began in 1983 and the first production missile was delivered in 1987.

The Museum's ACM is the 12th full scale development article. It was used for numerous captive-carry (unlaunched) test flights with both B-52H and B-1B aircraft. Tests of the missile software and systems integration with the carrier aircraft were completed successfully during those flights.

SPECIFICATIONS
Wingspan: 10 ft. 3 in.
Length: 20 ft. 10 in.
Body Diameter: 2 ft. 5 in.
Weight: 3,500 lbs. loaded
Warhead: W-80-1 (nuclear) warhead
Engine: Williams International F-112 Turbofan of 732 lbs. thrust

PERFORMANCE
Cruising Speed: Subsonic
Range: More than 1500 miles

**General Dynamics AGM-129A
Advanced Cruise Missile(ACM)**

BOEING AGM-86B AIR-LAUNCHED CRUISE MISSILE (ALCM)

SPECIFICATIONS
Span: 12 ft.
Length: 20 ft. 9 in.
Body diameter: 24 ft. 4 in.
Weight: 3,100 lbs. loaded
Armament: W-80-1 nuclear warhead
Engine: Williams International F107-WR-101 turbofan of 600 lbs. thrust
Cost: $1,000,000 (production version)

PERFORMANCE
Cruising speed: About 500 mph.
Range: About 1,500 miles
Operating altitude: Approximately 100-500 ft. above terrain
Maximum altitude: Above 20,000 ft.

The AGM-86B is an unmanned, air-to-ground nuclear missile launched from aircraft such as the B-52 or B-1. Powered by a small turbofan engine, the AGM-86B flies at high speed and low altitude, making it hard to detect on radar. The missile is programmed to fly to a preselected target by inertial guidance and by comparison techniques through which prerecorded topographical features are matched with the terrain "seen" by the missile's sensors. Each B-52 can carry at least 12 ALCMs, permitting a bomber force to saturate enemy defenses. The AGM-86B became operational in December 1982.

This AGM-86B, equipped for mid-air retrieval for economy reasons, made five flights between January 1980 and October 1982, accumulating more than 20 hours of flight time.

It was acquired by the USAF Museum in February 1983.

MARTIN CGM–13B "MACE"

The initial series of Mace surface–to–surface missiles, declared operational in 1959, used a guidance system permitting a low–level attack by matching a radar return with radar terrain maps. The "B" series, in service from 1961 to early 1970s, offered the option of high or low attack. Mace "As" were phased out in the late 1960s, but some were used later as target drones.

MARTIN TM–61A "MATADOR"

The Matador, first USAF tactical guided missile, carried a conventional or a nuclear warhead. Launched from a mobile trailer, it had a range of 690 miles. Development began in 1945 and the first Matador unit was deployed overseas in West Germany in 1954. Phase-out began in 1959 in favor of the "Mace."

BOEING CIM–10A "BOMARC"

The Bomarc was a surface–launched pilotless interceptor missile designed to destroy enemy aircraft. It was guided from the ground until near its target when an internal target seeker took over. Testing began in 1952 and the "A" series with a range of 260 miles became operational in 1960. Improved "Bs" entered USAF inventory in 1961 and were positioned at sites in the U.S. and Canada. Phaseout of the Bomarc was completed in 1972.

MARTIN X–24A AND X–24B

The X–24 series of lifting bodies, a joint NASA/USAF project, was designed to investigate flight characteristics within the atmosphere from high altitude supersonic speeds to landing, and to prove the feasibility of using lifting bodies for return from space. They are wingless aerospacecraft which derive lift from their body contours and aerodynamic control surfaces. They are designed to be launched into space by rocket boosters to ferry crews and supplies to space stations.

The X–24A made its first powered flight on March 19, 1970. It was carried aloft and released by a B–52. Upon release, the X–24A pilot ignited the rocket engine which boosted the lifting body to its maximum speed and altitude; then he maneuvered it to a glide landing on a dry lakebed. The X–24A made 28 powered flights at the Air Force Flight Test Center (AFFTC), Edwards AFB, California.

The X–24A on display was originally the jet–powered Martin SV–5J, a derivative of the X–24A. It was never flown. For display, the SV–5J has been converted to simulate the original X–24A. In 1972, the X–24A was rebuilt as the X–24B with a more stable external configuration. Its first powered flight lasted 6 min. 45 sec. on November 15, 1973. While the X–24B usually landed on an Edwards AFB dry lakebed, it was also the only lifting body to land on a conventional runway. It made its 36th and last flight on November 26, 1975, and was transferred to the Museum the following year.

X–24A SPECIFICATIONS
Span: 13 ft. 8 in.
Length: 24 ft. 6 in.
Height: 10 ft. 4 in.
Weight: 10,700 lbs. max. at launch
Armament: None
Engines: OneThiokol XLR–11 rocket engine of 8,000 lbs. thrust; two Bell LLRV optional landing rockets of 400 lbs. thrust ea.

PERFORMANCE
Maximum speed: 1,036 mph.
Maximum altitude: 71,407 ft.

X–24B SPECIFICATIONS
Span: 19 ft. 2 in.
Length: 37 ft. 6 in.
Height: 10 ft. 4 in.
Weight: 13,000 lbs. max. at launch
Armament: None
Engines: OneThiokol XLR–11 rocket engine of 8,000 lbs. thrust; two Bell LLRV optional landing rockets of 400 lbs. thrust ea.

PERFORMANCE
Maximum speed: 1,163 mph.
Maximum altitude: 74,130 ft.

McDONNELL MERCURY SPACECRAFT

Project Mercury involved six one–man flights (1961–63) to investigate man's ability to perform in space and to test basic space technology and hardware. The Mercury spacecraft weighs about 2,000 pounds and is nine feet tall. The pilot reclined on a couch contoured to his individual shape. During re–entry into the earth's atmosphere, the spacecraft's blunt curved end was the leading face; it was coated with heat–resistant plastics which burned away (ablated) to protect the crew compartment from excessive heating.

The spacecraft on display was flight–rated but never flown. It was used to provide parts to support the last Mercury mission, flown by Astronaut L. Gordon Cooper, Jr. on May 15–16, 1963. (On loan from the National Air & Space Museum, Smithsonian Institution.)

McDONNELL GEMINI SPACECRAFT

Project Gemini, which used a two–man spacecraft, bridged the gap between the Mercury program, the first tentative steps into space, and the Apollo program, which landed men on the moon. Gemini's primary objectives were to investigate the problems of long–duration spaceflight, to develop techniques for rendezvous and docking with target vehicles, and to conduct extravehicular operations. After two unmanned test flights in 1964, ten manned Gemini missions took place in 1965–66. Two of these, Gemini 6 and 7, were simultaneous so that the spacecraft could rendezvous in space and orbit in close formation.

The Gemini spacecraft weighs approximately 4,500 pounds and is 8 feet, 6 inches tall. The spacecraft on display, although flight–rated, was never flown, but was used for thermal qualification testing. (On loan from the National Air & Space Museum, Smithsonian Institution.)

APOLLO 15 COMMAND MODULE

At 9:34 AM EDT on July 26, 1971, a giant Saturn V launch vehicle lifted off its launch pad at the Kennedy Space Center, Florida carrying the Apollo 15 spacecraft. Aboard the command module were Col. David R. Scott, commander; Lt. Col. James B. Irwin, lunar module pilot, and Maj. Alfred M. Worden, Jr., command module pilot, comprising the first all–USAF Apollo crew. On July 30, the lunar module "Falcon," named for the USAF Academy mascot, carried astronauts Scott and Irwin to the moon's surface where they spent almost 67 hours while astronaut Worden remained aboard the command module in moon orbit conducting scientific experiments and photographing lunar landmarks. At 4:46 PM EDT on August 7, the command module splashed down in the Pacific Ocean 333 miles north of Hawaii, concluding the 12–day mission. Apollo 15 was the ninth manned Apollo flight and the fourth lunar landing.

Three major components of the Apollo spacecraft were a service module containing support and propulsion systems; the lunar module, a "space taxi" to carry two astronauts to and from the moon's surface; and the command module which served as control center and living quarters for the three–man crew. The latter was the only portion of the spacecraft intended to return to earth. The Apollo 15 command module, nicknamed "Endeavour" after the ship which carried Capt. James Cook on his 18th century scientific voyages, is 10 feet 7 inches high and weighed about 13,000 pounds at launch. Its outer shell of stainless steel honeycomb is covered with ablative or heat–dissipating material, the inner shell is aluminum honeycomb. The heat–shield on the base is made of a form of plastic (phenolic epoxy resin) which protected the crew from the 3000° Fahrenheit temperatures encountered during re–entry into the earth's atmosphere. The hatch on the side provided entry into the capsule while a hatch on top was used when docked with the lunar module. The command module was designed, developed, and produced by North American Rockwell Corp.

MUSEUM RESTORATION HANGAR

The Museum's Restoration Hangar is located in Hangar 4D about a mile from the main Museum complex. The restoration and preservation of aircraft and related support equipment in the collection is performed by the Restoration Division and volunteer staff. Many technical skills are found among these employees. In addition to working on aircraft here at Wright-Patterson, the division is called upon to provide technical guidance to other museums which hold USAF Museum aircraft on loan. They also provide quality control over work being done by contract on our aircraft.

Restoration tours are available to the public once a week during the months of June, July and August. Reservations can be made a week in advance by calling (937) 255-3286. A limited number of Restoration Tours are given during the rest of the year. Information on these additional tours can be obtained by calling the Museum's Information Desk (937) 255-3286 extension 303.

186

"Flying Tiger" Memorial

Memorial Wall

Security Police Memorial

MEMORIALS

The United States Air Force Museum Memorial Park provides an opportunity for individuals, veterans groups and various organizations to establish memorials to commemorate loved ones and to recognize achievements of the past. The most popular and inexpensive memorials on the Museum grounds are the Living Tree Memorials which include a tree, plaque and granite marker. All costs for the Museum memorials are borne by the sponsors. Those interested in more information should write to the USAF Museum for details.

WWII CONTROL TOWER
(8TH AF MEMORIAL)

This is a reproduction of the 1942 standard control tower representing 8AF control towers used in Great Britain during WWII. A weather detachment, manned by two forecasters and two weather observers, usually occupied a ground floor room. The flight controllers, who occupied the second story room fronting the balcony, provided pilots with weather information and flight clearances and directed takeoffs and landings. The flat roof often supported a weather observation point and weather recording instruments, such as a wind vane and anemometer. (Photos: S. Weaver)

188

NISSEN HUT

The Nissen Hut is one of the British temporary structures that served the Allied forces in England in WWII as housing, administration and work shops. The Museum's Nissen Hut was erected by the Royal Air Force near Saffron Walden, Essex, England on the Debden Aerodrome which became the home of the 4th Fighter Group, 8th AF, from 1942 to 1945. When the Royal Air Force abandoned Debden in the early 1980s, they donated two of the Nissen Huts to the Air Force Museum.

The Museum's Nissen Hut houses a realistic reproduction of a military club bar (the "Belly Tank" Bar) and a WWII Fighter Squadron briefing room.

The Nissen Hut is located next to the 8th Air Force Control Tower.

DONOR'S WALL

Outside the main entrance to the Air Force Museum visitors walk past a structure known as the Donor's Wall that recognizes "Patrons of the Museum." This artistically pleasing monument bears plaques of individuals and organizations having made major monetary contributions through the years. This is the first phase of a series of similar walls to be built in the future.

SPECIAL EVENTS

Biplanes abound at the WWI "Dawn Patrol" Fly-In

The Museum's annual Kite Festival is a fun time for the whole family

Radio-control aircraft enthusiasts display their models.

The U.S. Air Force Museum, often in conjunction with the Air Force Museum Foundation, sponsors various special events throughout the year. These include a WWI Fly-In, an annual Kite Festival, radio-controlled aircraft demonstrations, band concerts, aviation lectures, special aircraft acceptance ceremonies, and more. Call the Air Force Museum Public Affairs office for current details. Phone: **(937) 255-4704**. Also visit the Museum's web site at: **http://www.wpafb.af.mil/museum/**

AIRCRAFT INDEX

AIRCRAFT INDEX (Continued)

AIRCRAFT MANUFACTURERS